The
Southern Way

The regular volume for the Southern devotee

Kevin Robertson

Issue 52

www.crecy.co.uk

© 2020 Crécy Publishing Ltd
and the various contributors

ISBN 9781909328990

First published in 2020 by Noodle Books
an imprint of Crécy Publishing Ltd

New contact details
All editorial submissions to:
The Southern Way (Kevin Robertson)
'Silmaril'
Upper Lambourn
Hungerford
Berkshire RG17 8QR
Tel: 01488 674143
editorial@thesouthernway.co.uk

A CIP record for this book is available from the British Library

Publisher's note: Every effort has been made to identify and correctly attribute photographic credits. Any error that may have occurred is entirely unintentional.

Printed in the UK by Short Run Press

Noodle Books is an imprint of
Crécy Publishing Limited
1a Ringway Trading Estate
Shadowmoss Road
Manchester M22 5LH

www.crecy.co.uk

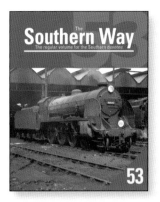

Issue No 53 of THE SOUTHERN WAY
ISBN 9781800350212
available in January 2021 at £14.95

To receive your copy the moment it is released, order in advance from your usual supplier, or it can be sent post-free (UK) direct from the publisher:

Crécy Publishing Ltd (Noodle Books)

1a Ringway Trading Estate, Shadowmoss Road, Manchester M22 5LH

Tel 0161 499 0024

www.crecy.co.uk

enquiries@crecy.co.uk

Front cover:
Rudgwick signal box on the erstwhile Guildford to Horsham line. Seen here in its later life and no longer serving its original purpose – all the point rodding and signal wires that would have emerged from the base having been removed; note though the raised walkway still remains. For the present the line remains open although it is probably some time since the concrete loading gauge in the yard served its original purpose.
Graham Smith/courtesy Richard Sissons

Rear cover:
Back to steam; No 35013 *Blue Funnel* approaching Basingstoke Platform 3 with a Bournemouth line train. Remember how exhaust steam would often gather in the void around the top of the smokebox – as a spotty youth I used to think perhaps the smokebox was leaking...!

Title page:
We are rightly taken to task on occasions on the lack of South Eastern area articles so apologies again as it certainly applies in this issue as well. One day...we do try! In an attempt to make up a little, here is 'O1' No 31258 at Minster part way through the 'Railway Enthusiast Club' EKLR afternoon tour of 23 May 1959. The stock used was advertised as being 'Two 1923 coaches and a 4-wheel brake van.' Somewhat curious as to why the latter might be needed and from the image it appears to be an ordinary covered van anyway. *(Answers on a postcard please...!)* The service had started at Shepherdswell (EKR) visiting the various collieries and when recorded here would next depart for Richborough Sidings. The final destination was Kearsney.
Graham Smith/courtesy Richard Sissons

Contents

Introduction

I am writing this during what is still the effective 'lockdown'. For myself it is now almost six months since I travelled by train let alone visited a heritage railway. I fear for the industry both national and preservation and it is to be hoped the present emergency will not result in a further 1960s type cull seemingly at a time when a rail revival was starting to take shape.

But enough of the political pronouncements. You don't want my opinions, this is a historical publication and indeed that is what is in store with what follows.

Whilst I am genuinely grateful to all, old friends and new who have allowed their articles, recollections and material to be used, I must say one of the highlights of recent times has been the access we now have to the full colour archive of Stephen Townroe. An introduction to this is given at the start of the piece and in consequence I will not repeat those exact words here.

What I will say though is that the Townroe family had the foresight to realise the historic value of the material. I know of at least two other major collections from former SR engineers whose priceless items remain under lock and key. This is not to criticise individuals (and wild horses will not cause me to divulge names or locations) but for the sake of history do please ensure these items are at least secure for the future.

In recent times I have been fortunate also to continue to receive a number of items for inclusion in 'SW'. Thank you all, I promise we will get around to using all (well most). Where we are short is in the following areas; reminiscences, signalling and anything much to do with the South Eastern lines. I regularly receive comment, 'more please on the SE', I promise if we had we would, but I hope we have made a start with some SEC (and also LBSC and SR) locomotive images by Peter Cleare later in this issue. Recall too the term I think used by a commercial organisation some time ago, 'Was your ancestor a railwayman?' (they were trying to sell a form of genealogy service). Well if that is the case and you have a few snapshots of your family member working then please share them, you never know somebody may recognise more and have a few stories to add. Be assured, we never pass on contact details without speaking to you first.

I must also thank all those who continue to write in wishing us well for 'the next 50 issues'. I will not be at the helm by then but for the present I am very happy to continue. Pressing keys and looking at photographs is a far from unpleasant pursuit.

Kevin Robertson

Unmistakably Havant with 'Terrier' No 32640 running around the branch train – the latter's coaches in the bay platform. From the angle of the photograph the cant on the curve is obvious, and yes it is correct, just look at the vertical line of the water tower on the right. Cant on models is a feature rarely, it seems, modelled. Not being an expert modeller I cannot comment why but it may have a lot to do with perspective and the small scales involved. Do we need an excuse for another Hayling Island or 'Terrier' image, I don't think so, but what is interesting is that No 32640 has the large tool box fitted to members of the class that had the slightly extended coal bunker. Sister engine No 515S (later 32650) had the same fitting during the short time it ran as an oil burner in 1946. (And if you want to know more you will just have to read 'Special Issue No 17' – due out around the same time as this issue.)

The S. C. Townroe Archive – in Colour

Regular readers will recall that it was with some sadness that issue No 50 saw the end of the 'Lost Archives of Stephen Townroe' series.

We had literally reached the end of the road with the b/w views and I know from the correspondence I received others had similar feelings of disappointment. 'The collection that keeps on giving' was how one reader put it and I think that really does sum it up; an archive which recorded not just trains and engines, but what was current at the time, unusual and also interesting. The chances of finding another similar archive was considered to be remote to say the least.

But what a difference a day makes. Or perhaps as a renowned Hollywood actor also once said 'I'll be back.'

Above and overleaf: No 563 in light steam outside the front of Eastleigh shed in July 1948. We know SCT took some black and white images at the same time but it is a joy to see the engine in colour from 70+ years ago. Possibly the gentleman standing with the Trilby is John Francis – see 'Rebuilt' in SW50 and the letter from Alan Kinge. Alongside is a Southern 'Mogul' in wartime black but with sunshine lettering. Careful observation of this reveals the tender to be fitted with an oil tank. Using a process of eliminations reveals this can only be 'U' No 1625 converted to oil in late 1947 and which reverted to burn coal just one year later. Notice the addition of the loco number in small letters at the rear of the tender of No 563 and that no steam heat pipe is fitted.

Well, we are back and with a vengeance, for again thanks to the Townroe family we have now been granted access to the complete COLOUR archive to use as we think fit.

The collection runs to over 700 views covering the period – and remember this in all colour – from 1938 onwards. Like the b/w, perhaps all may not be worthy of reproduction; there is inevitably some duplication and some non-Southern images taken on his various trips elsewhere. In addition we should not forget a percentage, certainly not all, were previously available as slides/downloads from Messrs Colour Rail whilst others have also appeared in books/magazines (including of course our own 'Southern Way Special No 10'). It is hardly surprising that over the years various editors and publishers were quick to appreciate the rarity of some of SCT's colour images.

What we intend in 'SW' is to continue with a regular feature of SR-related colour images in each issue. The odd one you may have seen before – bear with us on that – for on many of the slide mounts is written detail that was just not available previously; an image of a failed component for example having the date, location, and loco number involved. We know readers of 'SW' want detail and we will do our very best to accede to those wishes.

Left: **LSWR crest on the splasher of the newly restored No 563, was this painted by hand perhaps?**

As we start this new journey I must repeat my thanks to the family. I have no doubt the colour archive will find a new and appreciative audience both in this issue and those that follow.

Copies of the SCT scans – but only as they appear – are available for private or commercial use. Please enquire at editorial@thesouthernway.co.uk and watch this space for details of something else very special planned for 2021.

Above: '**E1' class 0-6-0T No 3** *Ryde* **running round its train at Cowes on the occasion of an RCTS special on a glorious 18 May 1952. This was a major event for those lucky enough to participate as the tour encompassed every one of the lines on the Island. Just four months later the first closure would occur; the Ventnor West branch from Merstone after which closures gathered pace until we are left today with just the short stub from Ryde to Shanklin in public use. (Plus of course the heritage line based at Havenstreet.) No 3 was only used between Newport and Cowes (and return), the rest of the Island lines in the hands of either W32 or W14.**

Right: **We may doubt SCT needed one of these!**

Five years later in May 1957 we have a view from the 8.40am Ventnor to Ryde service as it approaches Sandown. Certainly an 'O2' at the head but on this occasion no locomotive details.

The propensity for Pacific type locomotives to slip upon starting – and – sometimes – at speed is well known. The weight thrown backwards on starting results in less adhesion being available. The way the springs were adjusted also played its part. Slipping was something that affected all locomotives on occasions and indeed continues to occur on modern traction when the coefficient of friction that exists between a steel wheel and steel rail reaches a certain point. Of course other outside factors can influence the situation, 'leaves on the line' perhaps being the most well-known. Nowadays sophisticated electronics can monitor 'cause and effect' taking automatic remedial action when necessary. In steam days it was the Bulleid breed, particularly the original engines, that generated a bad press in this regard whilst poorly adjusted springs could mean one engine would start away without incident and the next machine slip and slide all over the place. The capabilities of the driver and the effectiveness (or otherwise) of the sanding were other features to consider as well. Recall too slipping was not necessarily just confined to starting, as per the occurrence that spelt the end for 35004 when travelling at speed and as described in earlier issues of SW. Here in these three views we see the result of a slip and consequential rail-burn caused, we are told, by a 'Merchant Navy' in May 1957. But we are not told where or what engine. All three views would appear to be on plain track – not a station or regular stopping place as otherwise we would expect to see oil, grease and ash between the rails. Sometimes the damaged rail could be ground or the area cut out, we may suspect SCT took the images as an example and perhaps because the engine in question may well also have suffered damage as a result.

 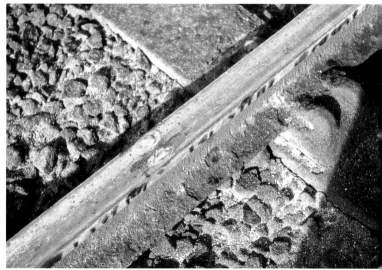

Fareham station looking north in 1955.

Right and overleaf: **Monday 7 February 1955 was the official closure day of two Southern cross-country routes. The first that from Hardham Junction through Midhurst to Petersfield, and the second the Meon Valley line between Fareham and Alton. With no public Sunday service on either line, the last regular trains had run on the previous Saturday. To mark the occasion the RCTS operated the 'Hampshireman' railtour on Sunday 6 February taking a circular journey starting and ending at Waterloo. In charge from Waterloo on the outward leg as far as Guildford was 'H2' Atlantic No 32421** *South Foreland* **whilst at Guildford a pair of E5X tanks, Nos 32570 and 32576 coupled bunker to bunker, took over. The pair had charge of the train from Guildford to Horsham (run round here which**

explains why the engines were coupled in the formation seen) and then on to the Midhurst line at Hardham Junction as far as Petersfield. SCT was on the footplate of No 32570 as the train approached Midhurst and then recorded the second view at Petersfield as the tank engines prepared to uncouple and a pair of T9s take over. Nos 30301 and 30732 ran south from Petersfield to Havant and then, bypassing Portsmouth, arrived at Knowle Junction via Fareham for the journey back to Waterloo via Alton, Frimley, Sturt Lane West Junction and the main line through Clapham Junction. For the journey over the Meon Valley line (photo stop at West Meon), SCT was on the lead T9 No 30301, seen here on the single line at Knowle Junction – the halt of the same name may just be seen in the background. (See article on Knowle in SW50.) Stephen Townroe was also a capable amateur artist and later produced a similar rearward looking view of the train whilst the special was in Privett tunnel.

The SR wartime headquarters at Deepdene House supposedly recorded in 1949 although we may perhaps doubt the date somewhat. Again SCT recorded images of the exterior and interior in b/w (which appeared in SW40 and 41) but this is certainly the first time we have ever seen the building in colour – appreciate it is early colour film so the colours may not be 100% true. (SCT used Kodak for a lot of the time, probably when it was available and certainly Kodak would appear to give the best and consistently good results. We suspect this pair of views may have been from a different manufacturer's product.) The reason for doubting the date is when did the SR vacate the building? Would it have been as late as 1949, we would have thought earlier. It would seem strange the railway still had need of such an outstation four years after the end of hostilities although Wikipedia notes that the house was demolished by British Rail in 1967. Whatever in the view that is clearly not lunchtime(!) we have a clear picture of the wartime extension added on to the end of the structure.

Another former LBSCR 0-6-2T 'Radial', this one No 32557 at the end of the triangle – note the substantial concrete buffer stop – at Eastleigh. No date but the first BR crest will be noted. The two men in the background would appear to be surveying – for the first diesel depot perhaps?

No 30285 inside Eastleigh shed and clearly under repair of sorts. Any ideas what are, and what was, the purpose of the pieces hanging from the boiler handrail?

A rarity and the only known original colour image of an oil-burning 'King Arthur'. This is No 740 *Merlin* outside Eastleigh shed in 1948. *Merlin* was the first of the true SR conversions of the period, emerging from Eastleigh in November 1946. After an oil-burning life of just under two years, the oil tank, burner and sundry fittings were removed and it reverted to coal in October 1948, being withdrawn in December 1955 following a deliberately-staged crash on the Longmoor Military Railway.

In October 1954 the tender axle of a new BR Class 5 4-6-0 fractured at speed 'somewhere on the Southern' – possibly near St Cross but this is not confirmed. The resultant axle was subsequently subjected to laboratory testing with the resultant flaw plainly visible.

Next Time: Bits that fall off engines; footplate trip Ferndown to Salisbury; rebuilding the flyover at Redbridge, etc., etc.

(W)13, formerly named *Carisbrook,* outside the rear of Eastleigh probably soon after its return to the mainland in April 1949. The nameplates had been removed prior to the engine leaving the Island and were subsequently attached to one of the final pair of O2s to be transferred, No W36, also in April 1949. The former W13 was now renumbered as BR 32677 and lasted until September 1959.

John Gaywood Click
'Engineering the Southern' Part 4

We start the penultimate instalment in John Click's previously unpublished biography with a little more on Bulleid's early days on the Southern as well as some comments from JGC on various engineering, workshop and drawing office goings on appertaining to the Southern.

To those who have been following previous instalments in the series, you will recall we have commented how his manuscript that exists at the NRM is by no means complete and in places is in effect little more than a jumble of notes, on occasions rewritten several times and most frustratingly not in any apparent chronological order.

Even so perseverance is (I hope) worthwhile, as JGC once again gives us an insight not only into the actual goings on from the time; but also with what I suspect was hindsight into the politics behind the scene both in relation to Bulleid's earlier time on the LNER, his move to the Southern, and subsequently Nationalisation.

The reader's indulgence is therefore requested if we appear to be going backwards rather than forwards on occasions for we start on the LNER and, before moving to the Southern and on to Rugby with the testing of No 35022, the later Giesl fitted to No 34064, and then Click's own departure from the railway. It might seem a strange way to proceed but be assured it matches the temperament of Mr Bulleid; and I suspect as well the same might be said about John Click! As before we have made minimal alterations to the text, restricted mainly to the addition of a date or a few words of clarification if needed.

'Anthony Bulleid has said quite lately that if Maunsell had not got into poor health in 1937 and asked to retire at the same time as General Manager Walker, he could have remained in the saddle until at least 1943. With the advent of war he could very well have been expected to go on for the duration.

That would have meant that Bulleid's chance of the Southern CME-ship would not have cropped up at least until Bulleid was far too old to be offered the post. Had that been so, OVB would still have been at Gresley's side, Gresley would not then have been overloaded as he undoubtedly was after Bulleid left King's Cross for Waterloo, and Gresley in his turn might have seen the war through.

I think this is a very plausible scenario indeed. Bulleid would certainly never have been given his head with Gresley a fit man; he had made plain his reluctance to do that before; BUT what would have happened if OVB had stayed at King's Cross and Gresley had only perhaps given up, say, in 1943?

Who or what would Sir Nigel have recommended to the Board? Would Bulleid have succeeded him? I like to think so. Perish the thought that Thompson could have beaten OVB to it – though he seems to have had a good deal of influence with impressionable directors; those delightful little books of expert engine diagrams for example! *(These are unknown to your Editor.)* More Pacifics would presumably have been 'out', but 'V2' building would have continued. But then how about the 'V4'? In retrospect, and given that the Thompson 'B1' was a goodish design, how would the baby 2-6-2 have fared under wartime conditions? One thing is certain, Bulleid would never have called on Stanier (as Thompson did) to report against the Gresley conjugated valve gear.

The plywood mock up covers the real engine, No 935 *Sevenoaks*. Rumour persists the engine made a trial trip as far as Micheldever in this condition but, in the opinion of your Editor this would seem highly unlikely – note too the cab windows are blanks! Had this morphed into a metal casing several points would have needed to be addressed, access for preparation and disposal being the most obvious. Even so a considerable amount of time must have gone in to reaching this stage and which has to be said, several decades later, does look somewhat dated.

Lord Nelson Class 4-6-0 No 857 with its unique large boiler at Bromley on 1 August 1938. The high domed appearance and curved firebox (compared with the Belpaire type fitted to the remainder of the class) is apparent to the rear of the steam dome. The increased diameter and the boiler and smokebox also necessitated a unique stepped design to the smoke deflectors, whilst the increased diameter smoke deflectors. *H. C. Casserley*

OVB never opened up on this topic to me in Dublin, contenting himself simply to saying, "I can never understand why Thompson did that." (At that time I am sure that Bulleid had never seen Stanier's report which was written by E. S. Cox who had done the actual investigation. The report did though come into his hands (from J. F. Harrison sometime in the 1960s). I have that copy here now and given that he was only doing what he was told, it seems both fair and by no means condemns the gear out of hand. Certainly ESC confirmed the view that irregularities in both outside gears were multiplied at the centre (that nobody denied) but pointed out that the pin sizes were a lot smaller than used in LMSR practice (and for that read GWR too) so that increasing their size and improving the lubrication would go a long way to overcoming the known problems. Thompson certainly read into the report what he most wanted to see – outright condemnation.

However, conjecture is all very well – it didn't happen, but Bulleid in charge of the LNER instead of Thompson is worth thinking about… . He would have had the authority for the first time.

Bulleid seems already to have known the (Southern) Chairman, Robert Holland Martin, and he recommended him to Sir Herbert Walker. The Southern's 'electrifying' General Manager conducted the interview but retired as the same day as Maunsell. It was therefore Gilbert Szlumper who was OVB's General Manager from day one. The Board had already decided to brighten up the Southern's image, so the new CME took that hint at once.

I don't think OVB rode on a 'Schools' in his LNER days, but he certainly recognised a masterpiece when he did. T. E. Chrimes called No 921 "the fastest thing on wheels", and Bulleid went to find out for himself on the Bournemouths and had No 921 indicated. It was Maunsell's 3-cylinder 4-4-0 rather than his 'Nelson' that got considered when the Board wanted

a 'new image'. "Why!" they must have said, "even the Great Western have engines with streamlined bits on them." Personally I had a sneaking regard for *Manorbier Castle* and altered my Hornby one with plasticine. The half of the forty 'Schools' that got Lemaitre exhausts, like this one, were only marginally better, sounded quite different, and were dirtier engines to ride on due to the softer exhaust.

Whilst Bulleid's earliest work on the Southern is often referred to as being his attempt at a 2-8-2 design we should not forget that the stock for the 1939 Gillingham and Maidstone electrification was on the boards in the Carriage Works at Eastleigh and it is in those two-car sets that we see his earliest influence: steel-clad bodywork making full use of the loading gauge width, spartanly simple interior design with six-a-side seating in the third class, and a new styling that was to last with little change right through to the older suburban units that were in service almost to the end of the slam-door stock.

With memories of his 1927 run on No 850, Bulleid was not surprised to find that the 'Night Ferry' had quickly got (with 55 tonnes a time for the Wagon-Lits sleeping cars) beyond the ability of a 'Nelson' so that its running needed two 4-4-0s. "Big engine wasted," he added.

Bulleid always said that a helpful method of judging ride quality was to write notes and compare their legibility. That seems to be borne out by those he made in 1927 when he rode on Maunsell's *Lord Nelson*, then just over a year old and still undergoing service trials before more were ordered. *(Bulleid was on the LNER at this time but was involved in the riding trials following the Sevenoaks disaster.)* Whenever the locomotive was running fast, yet "not really moving" as he might have put it, the writing then gets a bit groggy! Going down they had a 425 ton 'Golden Arrow' rake; but the return train, the 2.30pm Ostend up, was of only 277 tons. Perhaps that was why his notes afterwards started:

"The engine was never worked to any power, and appears to be too powerful for the work it is doing. The blast action on the fire was very steady indeed and no sparks were thrown. Boiler pressure was maintained, in fact care was taken to prevent the engine blowing-off frequently. The engine was driven on the regulator" – cut off was a uniform 25% throughout. "The exhaust injector was in use most of the time to maintain the water level. The tender rides extremely well but the design of the coal space is bad – the coal not feeding forward. Smoke and steam beat down badly"; smoke deflectors were not fitted until 1929. "The fireman found the long grate rather difficult and had to push the fire forward four times."

I can imagine OVB dodging the dreadfully long and hot fire-irons.

The fireman that day was Royal Train Driver Philpot. By the time he recounted this tale in the 1950s he mentioned that when OVB had ridden with them "he condemned the engine!" At least OVB put the coal problem right when he got the chance a decade later. That trip was no doubt arranged between the two CMEs (Gresley and Maunsell) at a meeting of the Association of Railway Locomotive Engineers.

Apart from war work and of course his locomotives that emerged from Eastleigh and Ashford at this time, Bulleid had also made a start on new locomotive-hauled coaches but the war prevented them getting beyond the underframe stage. Surprisingly, these were stored until 1944 rather than getting snapped up for some kind of war use. Bodies were built and complete coaches came out from late 1945, but were something of a hybrid, owing quite a lot, including length, to the Maunsell era though they did exhibit a Bulleid speciality, the attractive curved, flush sides.

The first truly post-war main-line coach, a prototype of course, came out in the summer of 1945 and looked marvellous. It was on a new standard underframe that made the vehicle no less than 67 feet 1 inch over buffers. It was also singularly clean-lined with large windows in the curved sides that OVB had already made his own both in locomotives and earlier vehicles. The new design was shown to the public for their democratic view on, mainly, whether compartment or open stock should be built in future. It even had electric underfloor foot warmers, a clear indication even then, that OVB was feeling the effects of hypothermia *(JGC's word)*, much to the benefit of his fellow sufferers. This prototype and all subsequent varieties of Bulleid's steam-hauled stock had steel-clad, wooden-framed bodies; and when asked why, Sanders said that unlike the suburban stock the numbers didn't justify the changeover.

When BR Standard Mk1 coaches came out they did have steel bodies but still on separate underframes. In my view, and it is shared by many, the Bulleid stock was imitated in the Mk1s yet the latter never quite achieved the sheer style that Bulleid did. His wife Marjorie, whom I never had the pleasure of meeting, often advised on decor and she must have had very good taste.

It must be said though that Bulleid was constantly trying to change details and it was much to the credit of those running the carriage works that any two vehicles emerged alike. A ploy, certainly used advantageously in Ireland to mitigate this problem, was for a compartment mock-up to be always available on which OVB could try curtains, carpets, lighting, upholstery and fittings to his heart's content, changing it every time he came down, and the more the better, whilst the production team simply carried on building!

Now for the *faux pas*. Who started the Tavern Car idea? I can't think it was OVB himself although the inside was a novelty that had commercial possibilities. I truly think he must, quite flippantly and without the slightest idea that he would be taken up on it, have said something, to Shepherd, perhaps, about the outside painting and hadn't the heart to say no when it got done: nothing else fits. Missenden was non-committal at first and had them shared out round the regions, but wavered in his support and then capitulated to the pressure when 'influential gentlemen' on the 'Master Cutler' said enough was enough – to *The Times,* no less. The turnover rate at times of high demand for lunch or dinner was just what was wanted although inside with the tables laid they did look (JGC's words) like a lord mayor's banquet set out in a mobile chicken coop.

The most handsome vehicles of all were those six-car sets for the Bournemouth line; whilst, for the most novel, we need to go back to a single vehicle, No 100s, built as a sleeping car for the Southern Directors in which almost everything was new and different. For its inspiration we need to go back still further to wartime boat building.

It is my belief that if OVB had never designed a locomotive he would be remembered for his coaching stock alone, for it was in advance of anything elsewhere at the time and set the standards which were imitated, but not improved on, in the first post-nationalisation Mk 1 stock.

During the war Bulleid had asked to be allowed to build launches at Eastleigh, "the biggest and the best" for preference, but things were a bit limited by the need to go out of the shop doors and then travel to their true element (water) by flat wagon. Now from the earliest recorded times boat builders had built upwards from a keel; but, no, OVB had different ideas. He would, and did, achieve better results by jigging the hulls upside down and putting the keels on last. The slight problem of turning them over afterwards was of no consequence; though the Admiralty Commissioners, after recovering from apoplexy, did point out that the method might not catch on for battle cruisers.

No 100s then was built like his boats, the two halves of the resin bonded plywood body were united at the top by a keel-like ridge member, whilst the lower sides met the underframe; making, for the first time, an inherently stable structure: beautiful. The rest of the dividing walls between compartments went in rather like the formers in a wooden aircraft, such as the Mosquito. The plumbing was well-thought-out, if not cleaned out, and Bulleid decided to take a shower, without knowing he was performing its christening rites before breakfasting with his fellow officers.

No 35005, fitted with the mechanical stoker, near Rugby – note the wired connections to the smokebox. The engine is coupled to the LMR Mobile Test Unit which could be set to replicate the equivalent of differing loads; hence the comment in the text of how the engine appeared to be working flat-out at the head of just three coaches. *J. McCann/Stephenson Locomotive Society*

A. B. MacLeod, who was Stores Superintendent, and aboard, said he only once saw OVB really angry and he had cause, after all, for the shower spluttered and issued forth a mixture of cold water, oil, copper swarf and pellets of solder. I saw this vehicle several times, in the up bay at Ashford, coupled to a similarly re-profiled utility van which had a noisy generator inside to supply essential services when parked in an otherwise quiet siding for the night. It became known that Sir Cyril Hurcomb considered No 100s the most comfortable vehicle he ever slept in. I chanced once to say this to my second cousin Percy Bennell. He roared with laughter; "Hurcomb," he kept saying –" he is in charge of the Transport Commission?" They had both joined the Civil Service together: "Pooh-Bah" Elliot calls him, so perhaps all in all he wasn't the best witness. Seriously again, the other most interesting feature was 100s's bogies – centreless and developed from those first used under the Co-Co electric, the first CC1. It became a pet idea of Bulleid's but his Technical Assistant L. Lynes, whom I only knew by sight, was against it, as they were in Ireland when he introduced it experimentally there later on.

Apart from investigating the riding qualities, Bulleid's particular interest would have been in this 4-cylinder loco's 135 degree crank setting (giving eight exhaust beats per driving wheel revolution) and in its general performance, remembering it featured long lap and high superheat – the latter not employed on the 'Castle' that had shocked King's Cross in the 1925 exchanges. He seems not to have spotted the deficient exhaust arrangements on this trip – the worst shortcoming of the Nelsons as built – but he put that right too later.

The best and consistently good work was being done by the forty 'Schools' class 4-4-0s, as simple to fire as the 'Nelsons' were difficult, well liked, not at all temperamental, economical, capable of sparkling performance, and present in enough numbers to be well understood by the top links from Ramsgate to Weymouth. They were, OVB found, truly a masterpiece; and swift…comparatively that is.

He approved of their three cylinders, whilst their beautifully regular beat was refreshing after years of syncopation. He held to his view though, that what was wrong with the Gresley 2 to 1 gear was that the outside valves could not be made to do what the inside one did; typical incidentally of his habit of always looking at a problem from an unconventional viewpoint, as well as one that increased rather than reduced power of course!

So, with Traffic's idea of a faster 'Limited' service in mind on the Bournemouth line, Bulleid was asked if a streamlined 'Schools' could be arranged. The worldwide craze for streamlining was in full swing. So how could it be done? Bulleid had seen how cramped the A4's smokeboxes had become with the Bugatti wedge front and didn't want to make that mistake again. He found that it would be possible to make a compromise, and at the same time make the loco look larger, if he brought a line down to just behind the front buffer heads; an angle that then got used on all 'air-smoothed' designs afterwards. The cab and tender front were similarly angled on the mock-up put on to No 935 *Sevenoaks* and were only dropped, one assumes, when word reached the Eastleigh Drawing Office that firemen willing to work at the slope were in very short supply! Drivers were said to be content provided their seats were reclined to match.

The first go looked awful; but, when smoke deflectors were added, the result was not displeasing IF it had to be done at all. Despite what has been written No 935 never left the Works in either style, bits would certainly have wafted away if it had.

The 999 emergency number had just been introduced, so my guess is that someone like Stephen Townroe had a hand in it: murder had been done! 'Sunny South Sam' was one thing, small, on posters; but nevertheless the 'Bournemouth Limited' did appear, in malachite green with enough 'Schools' repainted to match, in the summer of 1938 and it looked splendid. *(With hindsight it was probably unlikely Stephen Townroe had anything to do with the numbering. SCT was at the time (1937/38) only just commencing his career on the Southern and*

Weighed bags of coal ready to be loaded into the tender of No 35005 prior to a test run.

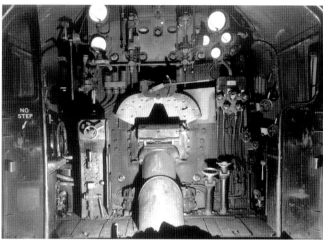

Mechanical stoker of the type fitted to No 35005. The engine is a 9F, No 92166.

whilst he would indeed go on to achieve high office it is doubtful whether he would have had any such influence at the time.)

According to JGC *Lord Howe,* as improved by Bulleid, was the best looking 4-6-0 ever built. Its special boiler was designed by Jim Allott in Maunsell's time and contrary to what has been reported, its firebox was not a steel one nor did it have a thermic syphon. A 'combustion chamber' gave it increased firebox volume and heating surface but it seems to have been something of a 'black sheep', despite its superb looks, for its lower tubes blocked very easily at the firebox end. Ash would accumulate quickly beyond the brick arch and assumed a cement-like quality when made wet by leaking tubes; which, if anything, was more of a problem than with the standard Nelson boiler.

Nationalisation. With Attlee's huge majority in 1945 it would be only a matter of finding parliamentary time before the railways were nationalised. Other more popular priorities got dealt with first so it was not until November 1946 that the Bill to do so was published. Before then little had been done to oppose the inevitable, but each Company now set out its future plans in the hope that attractive programmes might in some magical fashion dissuade the government from proceeding.

The Southern Railway was in the best position of the Big Four to carry out its anti-nationalisation schemes which, not surprisingly, involved electrification of its remaining main lines and the replacement of steam by diesels on subsidiary routes. The plan was a logical extension of the Southern's pre-war programme begun by Walker and only interrupted by the war. It took full account too of the findings of the SR delegation which had just returned from the USA (on the SS *Aquitania*) after examining rail transport there. New steam was not mentioned, though big orders had been authorised and more were to come.

Bulleid was a staunch Conservative and saw very clearly, if not before November 1946 then certainly afterwards, that his time was running out. Whatever he was going to do had to be done quickly.

On the other hand, I remember thinking that our Chief would certainly get the top job whatever form the new set up took, and the confidence in him was so high at that time that

the entire Locomotive Drawing Office took the same view. OVB, I feel, saw things more realistically.

The capacity of the Southern's works had been steadily increased during the war and was, at its end, greater than it had ever been; and wasn't it the policy of the Labour government to ensure full employment? The political climate was going to be advantageous in this respect at least.

Post-Nationalisation (JGC does not give a year) R.G. (Ron) Jarvis, who took over at Brighton Drawing Office, inherited the great team built up in the Bulleid days. Jarvis had been known to OVB as quite a young man before he left the LNER. Bulleid's son H.A.V. (Anthony) Bulleid served a pupillage at Derby, for it was certainly not the done thing then to work on the same railway as ones's father. He too got to know RGJ who was in the recently formed LMS Research Department. The two often travelled home at weekends together to Luton where OVB occasionally met Anthony. Jarvis then lived at Harpenden and OVB more than once gave him a lift en-route to Mackery End.

Once Jarvis was talking about the 'Leader' trials after I had found the copy of the final report on the engine. The conversation moved to the extraordinary performance put up on two occasions with 430 and 480 tons, the very last trials of all. Jarvis said he had tried to get Riddles to try a Leader boiler in one of the Garratts but without any success. He *(Jarvis or Riddles? – Ed.)* said that Hargreaves (who was Regional Metallurgist?) was told by OVB to keep away from these boilers during their later construction (I have also had a similar tale from Byrne) and as a result he was aggrieved. When his opportunity came he told Riddles in a report that the first boiler at that time in steam had a welding defect and that he considered it unsafe to work. I have never known the exact location of this crack (?) but it was in a place very difficult to inspect so I presume it to have been on the right hand side possibly where the siphon necks joined the underside of the barrel.

Concurrent with the 'Leader' trials were those involving a 'U' class. With the 'Leader' coming along it became imperative to have some form of smokebox cleaner. OVB opted for an open chute in the bottom. No 31896 went back after a 'general' to Redhill. Worked the 'County' to Reading loading up to 13 bogies.

Several members of the 'Merchant Navy' class were involved in trials of one sort or another. Aside from initial trial runs when new and after repair/overhaul, there were the Interchange Trials of 1948, those involving No 35005 and its fitment with the mechanical stoker, those involving No 35022 at Rugby and finally in rebuilt condition with the dynamometer car. Here No 35022 in semi-undressed condition is seen outside the testing shed at Rugby. This was where an engine on test would be disposed of after the day's testing had concluded or after a 'minor mischief'.

Strict instructions not to tell enginemen there was a six inch square hole. Working hard the air divided the exhaust in two; Dicky trips: Dorking Bank almost beat us several times; Time lost was made up down other side; Guildford stop then Pinks Hill; Fun with Reading men and white wipers; Considerable surprise that loco steamed as well as it did. Note was taken but 'Leader' was still fitted with a similar chute. Very soon it was blanked off on 36001 as well. *(What JGC does not mention is that on 36001 this chute, very necessary from a practical point of view, did seriously adversely affect the steaming on Leader as it would not close properly, bits of char and ash holding it open thus admitting air into the smokebox where there should of course be a vacuum. The Eastleigh test crew used to bring horse dung with them and smear this around the edges to effect a seal! – Ed.)*

Fire throwing by all 'Pacifics' was a problem and a test was arranged on No 34033 *Chard*. I was first to go out with the loco, new back to Stewarts Lane after a 'general' *(likely to have been December 1948- Ed. But later in his notes JGC refers to the same incident with the engine having been No 34031. To avoid further confusion we will stick with No '34033')* and bring back proof that it was steaming well. It did. She was then 'got at' at her next washout and a different chimney substituted. Who designed it I never found out, but a mesh of ⅛ inch rods was fitted at the chimney top, and another at the throat but this time at 45 degrees, the idea being that 'rockets' that missed one would hit the other: good theory. However, the rods reduced the free area throughout; so the loss had been calculated (clever stuff) and the diameters increased to make the loss good: wow! Unfortunately it was quite overlooked that if the blast nozzles filled the chimney earlier they would be unlikely to do so any longer. The unfortunate machine was instantly transformed into a mechanically good...dud.

We lost time enough to make an official 'failure' of it most trips; five minutes lost anywhere (even if regained later), or having to give the train up, was our definition of a failure.

Sammy Gingell actually knocked her about so hard one day that we only had 130psi running in to Chatham – in the down direction! My problem then was to get the thing off as soon as possible and hope nobody would want to tamper with the nozzles next.

Then someone touched a nerve by pointing out to OVB that the nozzle size for a 'West Country' shouldn't be 2⅞ inch but much larger at 2...inches *(again JGC has not completed the fraction – possibly for no other reason than his word-processor could not assimilate the figure needed)*. OVB was very chuffed as they say, and particularly pleased because it fitted in with his theory from the early days of the 'Merchant Navies' that their nozzles were designed for hauling 20 coach trains, and since Traffic never bothered to run such long trains, they must be over-draughted. His argument, however valid, was too late now, for everyone had got used to the smaller nozzles years ago.

Anyway, off we went. Yes, No 34033 did steam beautifully (but wasn't going to for much longer). So in went the new blastpipe cap, big nozzles and all. She stood 'Boat Pilot' at the Lane all morning and I went down with Tommy Twiggs on the 2 o'clock Boat. We were in trouble at once and losing time hand over fist. Even the people at Orpington Control Office were lining their windows and waving us on. That did it. Tom, not one to give up easily, announced he'd stop at Tonbridge and take a pilot. We just got over the top at Knockholt, managing to keep the brakes off, and with no water in the glass to speak of – even less when we looked downhill. She'd "come rarndabit," as Tom put it, by Sevenoaks; and after a long shut off we ran into Tonbridge where, as we stopped on the middle road with a bit of a jerk by the column, she blew off heartily, The local gold braid couldn't hear himself trying to think it out; and, clambering up, demanded to know why we'd stopped. "No steam, mate," Tom replied, somewhat paradoxically and with an engineman's scarcely hidden contempt for platform authority; adding since it was so obvious, "wot yer fink – want a pilot don't we." This absolutely floored him: nobody with a 'West Country' had ever asked for such a thing before, let alone one still furiously blowing off so raucously.

On the way we had made signs to the signalman at Orpy (Orpington) that we wanted a pilot asap. Unfortunately, he thought the sign made was some form of greeting! The Station

Master too could not understand why with an apparent surplus of steam why we had stopped. It was a sweltering hot day and when we'd thrown the bag out we ran it over each other, all the time looking to see where our pilot was. Eventually a 'German' backed off the shed, blower on, black smoke going straight up. He clonked on, we remade the brake and off we went. The damage – an unheard of 22 minutes. We pushed the German like mad up the three miles up to Tudeley and down through Paddock Wood we were really racing, but not really making much of a contribution by then, the little engine pulling us and the train all the way to Dover.

But if that was bad, worse was to come. We had been booked to take the empties back, but this was changed to the service Boat train at the last minute. Driver Dudley and his passed cleaner mate had arrived 'passenger' to work what they thought were the empties back. Through lack of experience on the part of the fireman we ended up with a poor fire (partly due to leaking stays) and a boiler that was overfull quite quickly, so we were priming in Shakespeare Tunnel. The fireman couldn't fire and couldn't stand either, we were losing time all the way. We were deemed a failure (by time loss) at Tonbridge with no steam or water. I tried firing and we really should have stopped for a blow at Sevenoaks. So, into Pol Hill and out the other side, the driver shut off as we went over the top which was just as well as there was no water in the glass and just 140lbs of steam; only just enough to keep the brake off. To make matters worse neither injector would pick up. Pumping the regulator at least circulated what water there was – thank goodness for siphons – and we eventually saw some water appear after Orpington but it then disappeared again until we were past Bromley. Certainly the closest call I ever witnessed. Spark arresters and occasional poor steaming were never really resolved until the Giesl Ejector was fitted.

Stewarts Lane, a shocking glory hole if ever there was one, saw me very frequently; but with enough problems of their own, I found it embarrassing to have to go and request stopping good locomotives to fit and then test some new gadget or other. How did they manage as well as they did? Richard Hardy knows.

As it worked out my first months in the Testing Section were little more than an extension of my three months 'freedom of the footplate'. I went everywhere on the engine (it appears as if he means No 36001 but this may not strictly be the case) and worked my passage as often as not. At the same time, I gained a much more realistic assessment of the problems of keeping Bulleid's locomotives going and came to have a great respect and sympathy for those doing just that in dreadful conditions of dark and cold, and with the very barest minimum of resources. The best equipment that sheds possessed were life-expired lathes, often thrown out by the Works. Nobody seemed to have the power to do anything about it. Hardly anywhere in the world, with the notable exception of the Norfolk and Western in the States, did anybody set about creating modern repair facilities for steam. Yet, when a film of the N. & W.'s monumental effort in common sense was shown to the assembled Institution of Locomotive Engineers in London, I was as disgusted as A. J. Powell was to see the reaction of so many who should have gunned for the same sort of thing

over here: they laughed heartily...although perhaps it was bitterly.

There was a lot else going on though, the most interesting being the mechanical stoker on No 35005 *Canadian Pacific* which I had unknowingly been in on from its earliest days.

Canadian Pacific with its mechanical stoker had two series of tests; both in conjunction with

Dr H. I. Andrews' outfit; the Mobile Testing Plant, consisting of LMR Dynamometer Car No3 and three mobile testing units. These last looked innocent enough but weren't the coaches they might be taken for at first glance. All their axles were motored, but as generators, and absorbed power put out by the locomotive on test, getting rid of it again through banks of resistors in their roofs so that the end product was hot air. Electronic equipment, advanced for its day, could maintain constant speed or power as was required. Whatever you did on the engine there was no way you could go faster than 'they' wanted you to – of that more anon.

The first problem was to test the whole caboodle itself. That's where No 35005 came in. Nobody then had a locomotive capable of sustaining such high power for long periods, or of increasing it suddenly as was possible with our steam reverser! The first 'tests' were run between Willesden and Rugby, giving rise to the falsehood that No 35005 visited the Testing Station there: it didn't, and we found out nothing from them but they discovered we had a locomotive that could skid their Mobile Test Units if they weren't very careful! When they came on to our ground it had been agreed with Waterloo that tests would take place to Salisbury from Stewarts Lane as 'base'. My rushing about suddenly stopped; I became the 'dogsbody' putting coal, tons and tons of it, carefully weighed out, into one-hundredweight sacks. These then had to be got onto the tender for each day's run. After a day or two I felt half dead, but in a fortnight I was as fit as I'd ever been. We had a 'crane' which fitted on the tender and was hand-operated. I would receive the sacks inside the tender and manhandle them into position on to the racks welded inside by about 7.30 every morning. An LMR minion then had the job of riding in the tender and tipping one of my sacks into the feed screw whenever it became starved of coal and pushing a button to record the fact on the dynamometer car record. He worked under a tarpaulin sheet lest he got his head knocked off; and complained, rightly, that if he slipped he'd lose his feet in that lean and hungry looking 'mincer' beneath him. I said I'd swop with him, and he was all for it, but we never managed it. After a bit I found a fresh supply of sacks and got ahead of myself so that whenever supply had exceeded demand (but that was prodigious some days) I had earnt myself a trip in 'the car'. If I didn't go the next happiest thing was to see the outfit leave as it is doing next.

At first No 35005 had standard blastpipe nozzles which tore fiercely at the thin fire, and resulted in a great deal more going up the chimney than was general with the class, and all threw quite a bit. Standing behind the driver there was a continuous rain of small particles, filling eyes and overall pockets. Goggles should have been mandatory – as in France. The coal used was 'slack', so small that to fire it by hand would have been completely impossible even with the 'Merchant Navy's' tolerant boiler. Someone did try, just the once...and came to grief – badly.

Whilst at Rugby if routine maintenance was required, such as a boiler wash out, the engine would be attached to its tender again and make its way over to the running shed. JGC comments 'We would then have a day's peace in the office.'

We opened out the blastpipe nozzles a sixteenth at a time until the loco got a bit 'dicky for steam' and then went one size back. In this condition with ... diameter* (* *The gaps are in the original manuscript. Clearly JGC intended to insert the actual figure at a later date but never did. Perhaps it was down to the limitations of his word-processor again!)* nozzles, compared with the original 2⅜ inch ones, steaming was wholly adequate and the fire throwing much reduced. The restaurant car people were pleased too; soiling of their table linen went back to near normal! Even so the amount of fusible ash was huge and it set as a more or less solid cake of clinker after the regulator was closed racing down towards Tunnel Junction. In those days locos were changed at Salisbury; but in any case she wouldn't have gone far beyond there. A rocking grate and a special ashpan were fitted later on; and, if used, somewhat improved the loco's effective range, but there was a real fear that an under-casing fire might result.

On shed it was then 'touch and go' to get the fire cleaned and remade, often involving pinching some live fire from another engine, in time to work the corresponding train home.

The locomotive burnt a lot of this rubbish coal and it would have been economic only if the Coal Board had let BR have it on a take-it-away-free-yourself basis rather than stacking it as 'unwanted' at the pithead. Even power stations with their low combustion rates and chain grate stokers couldn't handle the stuff. However despite one nationalised industry paying another nationalised industry the NCB had no intention of giving it away!

The trips to Salisbury were intended to be run at 50mph throughout and paths were arranged on this basis. Whilst the special notices said, "It is desirable that these trains obtain a clear run," that was not and could not be guaranteed; operations were always subject to instructions that might be given at any time by a Traffic Inspector who travelled with them and was of course familiar with the entire traffic pattern. If he saw a need for a change of plan, Dr Andrews would *please* do it: but of course *he didn't!*, one evening coming up the fast he decided he must take a Farnboro Indicator card at 10mph, adjusted the braking controls suitably and proceeded to get on with it, taking no notice whatsoever of the Inspector. The effect of this in the rush hour can only really be appreciated by those who know what line occupation was like then but a queue built up in no time; a Bournemouth, a West of England, a Portsmouth and so on all found themselves brought to a stand and crawling from signal to signal. The whole service reacted as No 35005, with Jack powerless to do anything about it, although appearing to be going flat out, crept through Raynes Park and on towards Wimbledon at funereal pace. Through Wimbledon eventually and on to the East Putney line she went before Andrews said he'd finished his card now, thank you! The damage was done, and when he had a good look at his card some days later it said, beside the myriad dots that characterised the quality of their indicator's work, "you will never again go out on the Southern!"

A hefty report came out, but to my mind it said nothing useful. We had gradually opened out the nozzles on No 35005's blastpipe so she no longer threw so much fine char out and felt we had got about as far as we could. We were burning 0 to ¼" slack and a lot of it! Andrews said shrilly, "we must test like with like," closed the nozzles down again, employed top quality coal which the stoker then reduced to near dust and then compared with hand-firing the same unbroken coal! The only conclusion possible was that at moderate rates the hand firing was more efficient and at the very highest rates it couldn't be hand-fired continuously at all. My own feelings are that if Traffic wanted much heavier and/or faster services, yes we could do it on, say, grade 2b coal, but special facilities for ash disposal would be essential and the scheme would have to be extended to many more of the class. Special table cloths and napkins for the restaurant cars, pre-dyed medium grey in colour, might also have been preferable.

What did Bulleid make of the mechanical stoker tests? Of course he felt the stoker should have been made to do what it did best and operated to make use of that ability. He never needed much encouragement to get on a favourite hobbyhorse about the misuse of *Cock o' the North* and how, "..it went from Edinburgh to Dundee, turned and hung about there," and seemed to have a healthy appetite, pointing out that a big engine is extravagant to keep in steam compared with a small one.

I am sure he quickly got tired of any new thing and wanted to get on with the next, he had proved a point. "Let someone else get on with it now, "and he expected that they would without any further prompting on his part. That attitude was repeated too often for it not to have been true; so did it come from his LNER experience when it always was up to someone else, whereas move away from Gresley and to when he was the boss and perhaps it was now down to him to do the chasing.

Bulleid followed Chapelon's teachings to a fault in proportioning the steam circuit as we have seen, but he was aware of what was going on in the other 'schools' of locomotive design. Next to French developments he was most influenced by work done in the United States. His 'Merchant Navy' boiler was capable of burning far more coal than any fireman could be expected to fire continuously for more than a short period. Bulleid knew this of course for the same had applied on *Cock o' the North*. Federal Law in the USA called for a mechanical stoker where grate area exceeded 50 square feet and they had become reliable and in general use.

The Railway Executive wanted full scale tests. Their real interest was to test the Andrews outfit, the No3 Dynamometer Car plus the Mobile Testing Units. Tests between Willesden and Rugby. (35005 never ran on Rugby Test Plant but the LTS supplied some workshop staff to assist.) Andrews wanted to test his units over their power range and No 35005 was the only loco capable of doing this. They wanted to know how the controls reacted to rapid fluctuations in power output. Thereafter the MTU was a competitor with other testing methods. 35005 did very well.

The Loco Testing Committee then further ordered tests of No 35005 itself on the Southern. Stoker versus the same loco hand fired. We complained that Andrews insisted the nozzles were to be similar for both series. Retrogressive. One day the brick arch came down, those in the test car never knew – or never noticed.

The results were predictable. Hand firing was more efficient at lower rates when using better coal. Mechanical stoking less good at low rates due to unburnt losses made higher by using excessive blast. The stoker made the use of poor coals possible and all coals possible at high firing rates. Stoker never failed either.

In normal service but with the stoker fitted and with remarkably little trouble, No 35005 settled down to working the 'Atlantic Coast Express' every day except Sunday, week in – week out. This was in the main thanks to Bert Plummer of Nine Elms who lived on the engine and having first mastered the special firing technique himself, saw to it that all the firemen in the top gangs became equally competent. I went on the 'ACE' once a week for several months and got quite good at firing her myself, and that experience was to prove very useful, twice over, in later years.

Bert would say very little and appeared to do even less. He'd stand with his back to the fire all the way to Salisbury and just once in a while have a peep in; look at his watch at Woking, say, and nod his approval to the driver; or now and again make a subtle change to the distributor jet pressures or to the stoker engine feed rate. He was a real master.

It would be fair to say that the MN, if re-scheduled to work at the higher rates, would have deteriorated far more quickly. Results put to some use in later years on the 9F similarly fitted. A Berkeley stoker was also fitted to the Turf Burner in Ireland and never gave problems there.

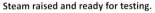
Steam raised and ready for testing.

Ready on the rollers. *Ron Pocklington*

Back with the Testing Section at Brighton, we did quite a lot of test work on Q1s too and one was particularly tedious.

Somebody had arrived at Waterloo with a 'brilliant' design of driving axle-box in bronze made in two halves with a vertical joint down the middle, looking on the end of the axle, held together by four strong horizontal bolts.

OVB was entranced and fell for it straightaway. Mechanical lubrication was, not surprisingly, essential; but the attractive theory was the absence of a break in the bearing surface anywhere; and, since oil would be arriving constantly, it wouldn't matter that there was no oil reservoir except in the carefully machined oil grooves.

About six of them were done, and every time one ran hot (and they did frequently) it meant a miserable day at Feltham or Guildford looking for the precise cause which was either no oil or too little or too late; but there was no way of being sure. The only sure thing would be a reprimand for not being sure.

We would check the mechanical lubricator, the pipes and hose, do our best for the journal, re-metal the box, bore it to recommended clearances, chip and scrape the grooves by hand, put the box together, replace the axle, couple up and prime the pump until oil was seen squeezing out, and Bob's your uncle – till next time; but that could, depressingly, be on the next trip. Then another failure was chalked up, the availability figure went down and we started all over again. I hated them. I might add that the Works did too; their 'new out' results were indistinguishable.

OVB was said to be particularly keen in making a 'go' of this 'experiment' as he preferred to call it; but, try as we might, nobody did. It was very difficult to feel one was doing much good on such occasions.

Only years later did I read that the Eastern & North Eastern regions actually fitted some A1 Pacifics with these boxes and had identically worse results, if you'll forgive that description. *(At this point JGC's notes refer to a 'File 31'. He comments, "File 31 was a magnet for me. It contained all the diagrams drawn whilst the Q1 was being designed. For example, there were about twenty-five of them – all lost now, unless they're*

at York still waiting to be unearthed. Bit by bit the Q1 (called C1 class until quite late) gradually changed from a cross between Maunsell's Q and a Bulleid-ised Lord Nelson to the eventual styling which most thought very shocking at the time. Doug Smith to this day admits with a little shame that he 'did' that "dustbin lid thing over the dome.")

In addition to our own home grown engines, *William Shakespeare* came off the South Bank Exhibition site as soon as the Festival of Britain was over and went straight to Stewarts Lane to work the 'Golden Arrow' service over the road I knew so well with our Pacifics.

Bill Grant of Dover took me down on the Sunday following No 70004's first full week's work on the Arrow; we were early at Bickley Junction without trying very hard and I photographed the train as we rounded the curve, "Eleven and two, Bill" I called. "No ten" he shouted back and then checked for himself. Traffic had slipped another Pullman on; it was a second eye-opener to be sure, and very hard to quarrel with the engine then, though all the rods did come off at speed on the up run shortly afterwards when the driving wheels, in a high speed slip, moved on their hollow axles. It proved OVB's view that anything that never failed was over-designed.

Merchant Navy at Rugby Test Plant. The 'Leader' had been so obviously hampered by having to do all its test work on the main line, that when I was offered the chance of going to the Locomotive Testing Station at Rugby it seemed by far my best, and possibly my last, opportunity of doing something for steam. No consideration had been given to putting the 'Leader' on test there though; and, even if it had, only one bogie could have been run for the Plant hadn't been designed for anything so unconventional or for six driving axles over a long wheelbase. However, Bulleid himself had a prejudice against stationary testing following his Vitry experiences and would certainly not have requested its use, though he had attended the opening ceremony on 19 October 1948. Then A4 No 60007 *Sir Nigel Gresley* was shown running fast, but at low power, as BR's tribute to his old and lamented Chief who had first advocated building a national testing station over twenty

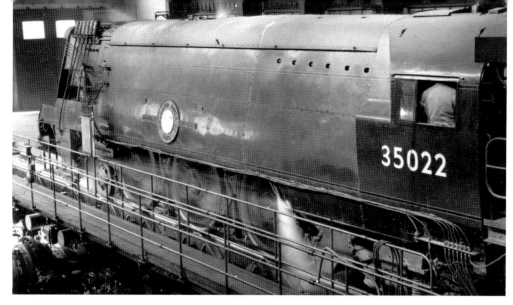

At speed but going nowhere.
Ron Pocklington

years earlier. No serious work was done on the 'A4', the aim being simply to make the wheels go round.

I hoped that one of 'our' Pacifics would be tested soon to find out more about their best features, such as the steel firebox with its thermic syphons and the multiple jet exhaust, and to look fundamentally at the known problem areas with a view to putting them right. That did happen later, but in a way that was not quite as expected then.

A 'B1' (No 61353) came for testing shortly after I got there and on it I began my long stint as the Plant footplate observer. The 'B1' was first to be tested as designed, then with a double chimney and finally with an SR-type multiple-jet blastpipe and large diameter chimney for comparative purposes. Castings for the last two were made exactly in the LNER style, and eventually went for scrap, because 'B1' work got overtaken by the desire to test a "strapping young lass down from Crewe" – BR CL7 4-6-2 *John Milton. (A comprehensive history of the test plant together with details of all loco types tested may be found at* http://www.warwickshirerailways.com/lms/rugby_testingstation .htm. *The same site also provides details of test records held at the National Railway Museum.)*

I confess to being enormously impressed by the 'Britannia', although I thought the copper inner firebox set the clock back years and would also have preferred three cylinders. I longed

for a chance to ride on one in its element out on the road after weeks of tied-up turmoil inside the Plant. That chance came when No 70009 *Alfred the Great* was crew training before working down from Euston attached to the Horwich Dynamometer car and two coaches full of Members of the Institution of Locomotive Engineers added to a service train. They were then to see No 70005 hard at work on the Plant and to return in the way they had come. When I joined Inspector Dan Drury on No 70009 at Rugby, they had already come from Crewe but without getting any water – the 'dip' *(JGC means the water scoop)* was useless; a vital pin in the operating gear had fallen out. The driver missed the column in the platform road; but Dan, not to worry, said "right away" – so off we went. We still had 300 gallons left after running non-stop to Euston inside the 84 minute timing then in force. I feel sure that we set an all-time record that trip, for the 158 miles from Crewe to London had been run on less than one 4,250 gallon tenderful of water with 384 tons of train. The ride was harsh and draughty, but the economy was a revelation compared with 'Scots' for example.

Before we produced the 'Britannia' Report (Bulletin No 6) we knew our next locomotive would be a 'Merchant Navy', and No 35022 duly arrived. Our Pacifics were looked on with awe and some foreboding in spite of the impeccable mechanical

Right and left hand sides with panels removed for attachment of test equipment. *Ron Pocklington*
(JGC and Ron Pocklington would meet again at Inchicore working for Bulleid on the 'Turfburner' – see next instalment – Ed.)

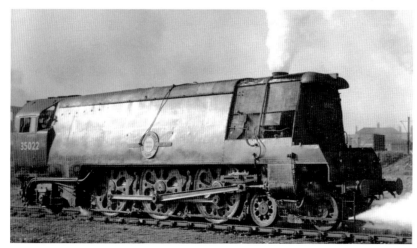

Back at Eastleigh and a moment of light relief. JGC stands on the framing of No 34003. No 32650 had received a recent overhaul and the Traffic Department were desperate to have it back for Hayling Island duties. However Chargeman Billy Casper was very reluctant to release it. To drop a hint a clay pigeon was purchased and strategically placed on the spark arrestor on 1 April as if it had nested. It worked and the engine was sent back soon after.

performances put up by both the large and small varieties in the Interchange Trials.

Before coming to Rugby, *Holland-America Line* had been through Eastleigh for a 'casual' repair and had received special attention to its tyre profiles and valve setting; but it had done over 185,000 miles from its last 'General' repair. *(or should that be from NEW?)* Its driving wheels were down to – little short of the tyre scrapping size – we wondered, by chance or intent? Might it even have been that the loco been deliberately chosen in some way? Whatever, there was no possible problem with the boiler though; it had been looked after by TIA all its life.

When it came to No 35022's first run ASLEF was on strike, and Alistair Lawson was expected from Brighton, so Chargehand Tom Potter drove and I fired. I was assured it was not strike-breaking; but I knew what it would do to my back. It served me right for I soon got in a mess and had to stop; 'Round One' lost with everyone looking on. After the loco and I had both had a blow we ran successfully enough the second time, but made a dreadful lot of smoke.

The regular fireman, Jimmy ("I know that!") Golding, got the measure of the beast the next time we ran and we certainly piled on the agony for him running up to a rate of firing well beyond what one was expected to handle. He didn't say a lot, but glanced at me once or twice with a look I knew well. By the time I was using both injectors and he was hardly getting a chance to put the shovel down, Jim yelled in my left ear "Wot you want with this engine is a ******** wheelbarrow and a ******** PLANK!" It was a saying that was to stick.

Slipping was going to be a major problem because any oil that got out didn't get left behind but gradually spread across the roller tyres until adhesion was lost. The invisibility of the enclosed motion and inside big end was greatly feared, but in fact gave no trouble whatever over a long period of very hard working. The programme was a long one; full performance testing in the 'as built' condition first, followed by a change to a single chimney and blastpipe The locomotive would then go back to Eastleigh to have its boiler substituted for one without thermic syphons. I must explain that it was extremely unusual for a Bulleid Pacific to be driven at full regulator for long, if at all, on the road. Enginemen from Padstow to Ramsgate had come to a similar conclusion; and they were right.

Full steam chest pressure could never be used at starting without a high risk of a monumental slip; and, once running, the miniaturised valve gear behaved in a prima-donna-ish way. For any nominal setting the actual cut-off increased with rising speed until the driver, faced either with making a very tricky shortening of cut-off by means of the steam reverser or easing the regulator, almost always opted for the latter.

Even when fresh from Works I always thought it unwise to run in a cut-off shorter than 20%; and, if that was done, it gave rise to vibrations which could be both uncomfortable to the crew and damaging to the machine itself.

Why, then, at Rugby did we run all our tests at full regulator? Well, it was theoretically correct and certainly cut out one variable, that of steam chest pressure, but took little account of a great deal of practical running experience with a large number of locomotives over a period of years.

The enclosed valve gear was a bold move at the time it was done, and a very logical one, yet it produced more problems than it solved. If, overall, its enclosure was unsuccessful then the fault was in the execution and not in the idea itself. Bulleid contended that later developments in sealing materials, and particularly in 'O'-rings, should have been applied retrospectively, in a really determined effort to prove his original point. That would have been worth doing, I feel, had a less erratic valve gear been hiding inside. However, whilst No 35022 was at Rugby all that had to be done was to check the oil bath oil level, and top it up occasionally, and to try the sump bottom cock for water, both being done

No 34064 fitted with the Giesl ejector and in steam. Sitting on the casing to check on the evenness of the blast are JGC and Dr Giesl. (Dr G had done this before at Rugby with No 92250, something JGC had witnessed. As he put it 'I was determined not to miss the chance this time.') JGC continued, 'Stunts such as this were good for morale and a lot of people were cautiously peeping from behind cover.'

weekly. We lost little from the oilbath, so the rather excessive amount that did get onto the rollers came from the cab wick-fed axlebox and axlebox guide oilboxes. We were loath to cut this down in view of the high power usually being demanded lest we ran into an epidemic of hot boxes by paring it down too much.

The steam reverser was prevented from its well -publicised habit of wandering by inserting a suitable sized collar at the reverser itself which gave us the repeatability we needed though it effectively meant we were limited to running at a fixed cut off all day, though not at starting of course. Subtle adjustments by the usual means would have caused all sorts of problems with the plant brakes. As it was, a very small change in boiler pressure would sometimes give rise to a disproportionate power increase; an effect that would occur quite unexpectedly and then disappear just as unpredictably. Had he been there (but he never was), OVB would have smiled disarmingly and quietly made the point that anything which resulted in more power was to be applauded. I wonder if Riddles ever thought of inviting him over; but I don't think he did. Had he been given the chance I feel sure OVB would have come.

It didn't take us long to establish two main facts: firstly that the boiler was a great steam raiser, with an efficiency very similar to other large boilers, but the virtually continuous production of excessive smoke (except when burning top-grade Welsh coal) indicated where improvements were badly needed. Secondly the cylinder efficiency was lower than it should have been.

This only confirmed everyone's general impression that the boilers gave freely and that it was the front end that tended to be wasteful. We found that we got a strangely-shaped set of tractive effort/speed curves as per the on-road tests with stoker-fitted No 35005, but everything we did confirmed the locos' well known ability to run freely at all speeds and to have great reserves of power that could, at a price, be called on at any time.

Bulleid often said that thermal efficiency never sold a locomotive; consistent performance and, above all reliability, was the imperative in successfully running a railway. His point was that fuel costs are only a small proportion of total expenditure per revenue earning ton-mile. Sam Ell, of Swindon, once derived a formula to substantiate this very point but there were so many

components in it that it seems nobody ever put it to any use!

If the multiple-jet chimney had been put on the 'B1' I think we would not have gone through the farce of trying the single chimney on 35022. Who knows, large diameter chimneys just might have got past E. S. Cox and become fashionable. There was a history, though, for No 35019 had been roaring about fitted with one, but with a success that was more apparent than real. The fact that it made much more noise should have rung bells, but it didn't. Rather, like No 865 Sir John Hawkins with his 90 degree cranks (and, consequently, four huge beats instead of eight moderate ones), enginemen liked to hear their charge barking. By the time we came to fit No 35022 with its single chimney we had given up attempting to find its maximum steaming limit but knew that it was at around the 44 to 45,000 pounds per hour mark – a prodigious output and a 'Rugby All Comers Record' had it been possible to avoid a slip long enough to prove it beyond doubt.

Any locomotive at full power at Rugby was a spectacle – but No 35022 was something apart. Two firemen shovelled without any significant pause from alternate sides of the footplate prompted by my foot on the Ajax fire-door pedal; every time the doors opened in went coal. Some people imagine that a fluidised bed is something new; they should have seen ours. Both injectors were on, one continuously and the other only off for a matter of seconds at a time, whilst from the chimney there was a continual stream of live fire. The smaller rockets made it into the smoke corridor in the roof; but the larger and heavier ones went up so far up and, returning, bounced off the smokebox top in all directions like tracer shells. The technical assistant taking readings of smokebox vacuum said he knew what it must have been like in the last hours of Pompeii! Protective head gear hadn't been invented in those days.

So: what happened when the single chimney went on? Well, in round terms the maximum steaming rate was carved down to under 30,000 pounds per hour at the expense of doubling the blast pipe pressure at that rate. No wonder No 35019 made a noise, but why then hadn't that loco been in trouble on the road? The answer can only be that it was never called on to steam for any length of time above its reduced capability.

Stopped in Wallers Ash loop. JGC is on the right framing with Harry Frith, the erecting shop foreman, on the ground below. Seen from ground level the oblong shape of the ejector shows up well.

Dr Giesl in the cab of the engine.

What might have been. No 34023 temporarily masquerading as 'O. V. Bulleid' in the sidings at Eastleigh, 1963.

Sam Ell was next invoked and the offending chimney was raised and the blastpipe lowered and several nozzles tried but nothing would touch the original. Bulleid would have smiled again, but without any malice. It was only me that wanted to say I told you so. By good fortune I got that chance later, at Brighton, and the same mistake was avoided during the 'modifications'.

Still on the subject of testing but some years earlier when Bulleid was with the LNER and stayed in France with *Cock O' The North*, Bulleid would have felt completely at home. He liked the French for whom he had great regard born of Freinville and the First War, and of course he spoke French fluently; but perhaps their sympathy was for him here. It is three o'clock one afternoon and running has stopped for the day: why, I wonder? Could it be that No 2001 had run hot again? Heated bearings were more of a problem there than at Rugby it seems and Bulleid once stopped No 2001 when he saw a driving axle-box cover stop vibrating as the white metal began to become 'pasty' and wipe. At Rugby I could tell from the footplate if a bearing was 'going' on a BR Standard by the smell of burning worsted; if we stopped at that stage no damage was done to the axle-box journal. At first it would not be obvious which box was in trouble, but after ten minutes or so the axle end had warmed through and the vituperation from the Swindon element about stopping the engine unnecessarily was seen to be un-called for. Rugby Loco Testing Station followed the French model very closely but was not opened until 1948 when OVB was there with many others including Armand, Ivatt and Peppercorn. OVB's Vitry experience seemed to have prejudiced him in favour of road testing for only when No 2001 went out with a dynamometer car between its tender and three old Paris Orleans 4-6-0s acting as counter-pressure braking locomotives was it possible to develop high power without risk of damage. An Est 4-8-2 behaved similarly, but the *Cock* was different in one important respect. OVB could tell if it was running at Vitry "...soon after leaving Paris by the smoke being made: with the French engine it was impossible to tell!" It was rather the same with No 35022; the Station Master once rang up D. R. Carling at Rugby to say, very politely, that the black smoke we were making was so bad that he would have to institute fog working in the station area if we went on. We stopped for the rest of that day.'

How long Click remained at Rugby we are not told. We know he spent some time in Ireland with Bulleid working on the Turf Burner but by the early 1960s had migrated to Eastleigh as Assistant Works Manager. It is here that two final events took place involving steam. The first was the fitting of a Giesl ejector to No 34064 Fighter Command. *JGC again takes up the story.* 'When steamed for the first time in steam Dr Giesl and myself sitting on top to check the evenness of the blast across the chimney. Dr G. had done this at Rugby with No 92250 and I was determined not to miss it here. Stunts (and this one did do a necessary job) were good for morale now and again and a lot of people were peeping from behind convenient cover, but an apprentice, one Ron Puntis (subsequently famed on BR), was bold enough to shin up a lamp post! "It'd better be a good one" I told him, and it was. Next day

we went on a trial to Basingstoke, stopping at Micheldever for Harry Frith to "have a feel round, look."

Mr Bulleid, now living in Devon, often came to London where we would talk locomotives at the Athenaeum for hours on end. He followed, with particular interest, the fitting of No 34064 with the Giesl Ejector. It also enabled us to fit a spark arrester without ruining the steaming. That it would do the job was a certainty – the only problem was overcoming the very unfair prejudice left after the Rugby tests of an ejector on a class 9 2-10-0 (*not explained by JGC – Ed.*). In service No 34064 was a cracker, it threw no sparks, and, as we had bargained, lifted its smoke in a way that none of the other 139 engines did, altered or not.

Almost the last thing I did at Eastleigh before being sent to Derby, where I only stuck it for a few weeks, was to take No 34023 over to a quiet spot behind the shed and cover up its true nameplate (*Blackmore Vale*) with the small-sized pattern on to which new letters were tacked. No 34023 was the last unmodified 'pacific' to have a 'general repair' and was therefore in the best condition of the few left at the end of steam; hence she was chosen for preservation on the initiative of Driver Alan Wilton, and others, then of Nine Elms. Bulleid was keenly interested and had a lengthy correspondence with Wilton; but he, bit by bit, lost control of the project he had started.

It seemed only right to me that the engine should be permanently renamed following the precedent I had set and I felt sure it would be done; but the Bulleid Society ponderously put it to the vote. With only one possible answer, and one matter of detail to settle (whether to be more familiar than I had been and go for 'Oliver V. (or V.S.) Bulleid') the unbelievable happened – the membership decided not to do it and sent OVB the magazine saying so. He didn't complain but simply said in his next letter, after I had told him what I felt, "I would not expect to be honoured in this way until I am dead."

One final comment not perhaps well-known was that the rods for the Light Pacifics were, at the start at least, made at Ashford – and to the wrong length – the trailing rods were three inches too long. But they were not wasted. By changing them side to side and making new, non-standard, rods with the joint pin ahead of the driving crankpin the costly mistake was rectified. Rods got changed between individual engines over the years, for example No 34051 *Winston Churchill* still has the joint pin in front, likewise No 34092 also did at one time. How many sets were involved I am not sure, but it was about twenty. A minor mystery too, is what was done with the first, or second, engines coming off the Brighton production line whilst new rods were being forged, machined and fitted. I remember the forge at Ashford working all night for some weeks: the thump of its harmers could be felt all over the town. *Exeter* could have run trials as a 4-4-2-2 but it certainly didn't. It was amazing what the works could do when they had to; so perhaps the simple answer is that No 34001 was delayed for the week to ten days needed. OVB would have been sad at the delay, but not furious.

In the final instalment of these reminiscences, scheduled to appear in SW53, we will deal with the time John Click spent with Bulleid in Ireland on the 'Turf Burner', in effect 'Leader MkII.'

The Horsebridge 'Ironclad'

David Lindsell

'The carriage now arriving at Platform One at Horsebridge station is the 1pm from Stoneymarsh, Mottisfont...' The image shows the arrival of a former London and South Western Railway 'Ironclad' carriage for restoration at Horsebridge Station in Hampshire in 1987. It was driven up the old Sprat and Winkle line trackbed from Mottisfont Station site by a Haulage Contractor from Essex, who in turn had transported the carriage from Branksome Depot in Bournemouth, where it had been part of the former breakdown train unit. Purchased for £2,000 from British Rail, plus £1,500 moving costs, by Val and Tony Charrington who then spent some £30,000 restoring the coach.

The Charringtons had bought the former Horsebridge station from Hampshire County Council in 1985, who had acquired it from British Rail (Southern) as part of the trackbed, to enable the Test Way Footpath to be built. They then proceeded to restore the site as it would have appeared in Southern Railway days, starting from a somewhat derelict condition. The station, which became Grade 2 listed in 1986 by Historic England, was opened on 6 March 1865 and closed to passengers on 7 September 1964.

On arrival the coach was transferred to a specially prepared length of track which had been laid, by two railway workers, one from Winchester and the other who worked on the MidHants Railway. Externally, the coach was initially restored to LSWR colours but later reverted to Southern Railway Green to match the décor of the station.

Above: **Similar vehicle, this is S728S believed to be at Clapham Junction.**

Right: **ADS226 along with its associated packing van at Branksome in May 1985.** *Mark Jamieson*

To complete the scene, many of the station artifacts came from local Southern stations, such as signals from Weymouth and a bufferstop from Eastleigh. The signal box is from Yalding Station in Kent, the original having been taken down with the well-intentioned aim of restoring it as a railway/hobby room in the rear garden of a house in Swaything. The porter's barrows came from Winchester.

Very nearly 100 years ago, in July 1921, the vehicle was built at Eastleigh as a Third Class Corridor coach to diagram 24. Initially given the number 773 this was soon changed to 717 when it became part of Southern Railway set 431. 'Ironclad' carriages were built to improve comfort for travellers using the Bournemouth line expresses and were in use on the prestige services for many years, that is until superseded by Maunsell and later Bulleid and BR Mk 1 stock. The nickname 'Ironclad'

Arriving at Horsebridge on a trombone semi-trailer hauled by a Volvo F88 tractor unit. Fortunately at this stage there was an amount of ballast remaining on the trackbed.

came from the construction of steel panelling and double framed bogies. They also had more generous dimensions being 57ft long, 9ft wide and 12ft 6ins high.

Cascaded onto lesser duties as time passed, No 717 was withdrawn from passenger service between 1957 and 1959, as indeed were many other similar vehicles, but then took on a new life as part of the Breakdown Train Unit (BTU) Staff Coach at Bournemouth Depot, numbered ADS226.

Once installed at Horsebridge and restored, the carriage was used as an overflow dining area and for dinner parties

taking place at the station. In 2018 the carriage was re-restored internally and is currently being used as two-bedroom luxury self-catering accommodation. Details of the accommodation available can be found on the Mulberry Cottages website. https://www.mulberrycottages.com/cottages/sprat-and-winkle-m555057 No doubt with this use it will survive for many more years after its centenary in 2021.

Restored to LSWR livery, looking south towards Mottisfont and Romsey. At this stage it was being used as dining accommodation.

In its current guise as self-catering accommodation.

Eastleigh Fireman

Vernon Jones

Across the rear of Eastleigh shed, a still serviceable 'S15' and a 'Battle of Britain' that is probably not long for this world. Vernon worked on both types of engine; whilst in the background is the coaling stage, somewhere he also got to know well. *Peter Elliot*

°In March of this year we received a note from Vernon Jones asking to be put in touch with John Stubbington, a previous contributor to 'SW'. We are always delighted to do this if we can although we would also always check first before passing on contact details. It appears Vernon knew John through their joint time as firemen at Eastleigh. Well of course we were then bound to ask Vernon for his own recollections...

As a young lad, I was a keen trainspotter, belonging to the Ian Allan Trainspotting Club and travelling all over the country with a group of like-minded boys, organised by local stalwart Jim Jackson. Meeting at Eastleigh shed every Sunday, we travelled as far afield as Derby, Exeter, Rugby and Bristol as well as visiting all the London sheds.

On leaving school aged just 15, the careers advisor had an apprenticeship as a tile fitter lined up but the prospect did nothing to excite me. So, whilst waiting for something more appealing, one day I cycled to the loco sheds at Eastleigh where I bumped into a lad I knew from the year above me at school, Charlie Thorn. He told me that there were plenty of jobs available there so the next day, I went to see Mr Hale, the Shedmaster, who offered to start me immediately as a cleaner on £3.11s a week. I recall the date as well, 4 April 1961, two weeks after my 15th birthday. Eastleigh, it seemed, was always short of staff, a situation that only got worse as time marched on towards the end of steam. Indeed, while on the subject of staff shortages, albeit jumping ahead somewhat, this shortfall did not just apply at Eastleigh, for I recall being sent to relieve at Nine Elms, travelling there and back on the cushions and working the Waterloo – Clapham Junction carriage duties upon arrival. Another time I relieved at Salisbury and I also recall getting as far as Westbury ready for a stone train from Merehead, something I was really looking forward to. Unfortunately the duty was cancelled at Westbury and going to the quarry was something I never achieved.

As the junior I was to become the messenger boy (known as the 8.28 messenger) because of the morning start time, riding in the train (sometimes in the cab if I knew the driver) from Eastleigh to Southampton Terminus Station and walking into the docks to collect paperwork from the loco shed there to take back to Eastleigh.

The depot at Southampton Docks (sub shed of Eastleigh), 4 March 1961. It was to here Vernon would venture when in the lowly position of 'messenger boy' although the role did have its compensation as he would sometimes ride on the footplate between Eastleigh and Southampton. *Tony Molyneaux*

An 'H15' on a down boat train, including Pullman cars, near Otterbourne. In the opposite (up) direction Vernon had his first practical training on a stopping goods service between Eastleigh and Basingstoke. *Tony Molyneaux*

'M7' No 30130 being turned on the Eastleigh turntable – the man and his hut are also visible! The largest engines would have to use the triangle at the rear of the shed. *Tony Molyneaux*

On Thursdays, two of us would walk to the bank in Eastleigh, opposite the station, with a big leather holdall to meet the Paymaster from London, returning with him by taxi with all the cash for the staff wages to be paid out. This was quite a nice little job and a welcome reprieve from cleaning engines! As soon as I was 16, I had two weeks training and passed out as a fireman and thus began my career proper – on the footplate.

This training was 'on the job'; two weeks of riding on the footplate with driver Bill Fair and fireman Norman Cox intended to learn the skills of firing an engine. I also had to learn the footplate rules from the issued rule book. I recall one trip as being on an H15 to Basingstoke. Leaving Eastleigh we first stopped off at the Otterbourne Water Works siding to deposit two wagons of coal, thence on to Winchester to pick up some vehicles which involved some shunting, finally arriving in Basingstoke, ready for our tea-break. We then worked an ex-Feltham freight train back to Eastleigh with a Q1. The best way to learn, on the job!

There were no written exams to qualify as a fireman but at the end of the two weeks I was supposed to go up to Mr Dare's office (who had taken over from Mr Hale) but as he was unavailable, foreman Fred Pope gave me a verbal test on the rules from the BR Rulebook. I also had to name all the rods on a Nelson class engine, using the big sepia photograph hanging on the office wall – which is now proudly in my possession, saved from the demolition gangs, years later.

One of my earliest memories was of going to Bishops Waltham shortly before it closed with driver Ron Walker on an M7 and about four wagons. The shunter rode with us on the footplate and was allowed to do some of the driving. On this same turn, another driver, Arnold Hiscock – a keen gardener – would stop the engine and its freight train on the main line between Eastleigh and Botley, climb down and dig up dog roses from the trackside to use as root-stock for grafting on to his own prize winning plants. It was like a scene from the film 'Oh, Mr Porter'!

At Eastleigh one of the first jobs I undertook was watering, coaling and turning the engines if needed. When we were busy, the drivers would let us do all of this on our own, quite a responsibility. We had to take the bigger engines to the triangle, to perform a sort of three-point turn so they were facing the right way for their next duty. The smaller engines were driven on to the turntable. A man emerged from a shed and operated it using a vacuum system, this being his sole responsibility.

Other duties might involve working to Winchester, Chesil, Newbury – well, as far as Worthy Down (see later), and Alton. Most of these were routine, you booked on duty, found your driver and engine, prepared, left the shed and worked the turn. There was also a duty to Alresford during the watercress season. We would take a Standard class 4 light engine to Alresford to collect one or two vans. There was always plenty

Preparation and disposal duties at Eastleigh. The covered walkway led to the enginemen's lobby and signing on and off points. A number of coal tubs are prominent in the foreground. *Tony Harris*

of time to wait while they were loaded with crates of freshly picked watercress so that was the ideal opportunity to head for the pub – firing an engine was thirsty work so a pint and a game of darts was very welcome, even at the tender age of 17! Returning to Winchester the vans were detached and left ready to be attached to an up train. We then returned light to Eastleigh, to clean the fire and book off.

There were five links at Eastleigh – we used to refer to them as 'Gangs'. One was the 'P&D' (preparation and disposal); the work was as the name describes – to dispose of ash/clinker, etc, from an engine arrived on shed and then prepare and place it ready for its next duty. This latter point would determine which way the engine was left, facing up or down. At times there was frenetic activity and others when, with all the work done for the present, there would be the opportunity for a card school in the mess room. I used to do quite well at this, regularly being up by anything from 2/6d to 10/-. Little did the others know I had become skilled by being brought up in a card –playing household at home!

A turn I used to enjoy was at 00.01, getting the upmail train to Winchester to light up the 'Winchester Bug' which was B4 No 30096. This was considered a creepy job by some of the lads who had been convinced by the older men that the old shed at Winchester was haunted. I had to get the fire

going first then oil round the engine for the driver Frank Mills, who was a 'Not to Go' driver. Because of a disability he walked using two sticks, he could still work but was not allowed main-line duties. Then I had to coal and water the engine before getting relief at 07.30hrs when I could return to Eastleigh shed and sign off.

I had been a spare man for a few weeks when the foreman asked me to do a turn to Basingstoke. On arriving in the yard, a Nelson pulled in with 15 vans on. I explained to the driver that I'd never fired on a Nelson before and he simply told me 'You'll be all right, my boy.' He nursed that steam engine – and me – all the way to Basingstoke, telling me just where to put the coal on the fire, his patience and kindness were much appreciated.

One day, as a young fireman, several of us were again spare men waiting in the mess room to be called for duty. The foreman came into the rest room and told a couple of us that a War Department engine had come in from Banbury to Eastleigh with an Esso tank train. The fire badly needed cleaning, with 3-4 inches of clinker all over the grate. There was no drop-grate on these engines unlike many of the ones we were used to, Merchant Navy, West Country and Standards.

Instead the task was done with a clinker shovel. So bad was the condition of the grate it took the two of us almost three hours to complete.

Matt Sacree was one of my regular drivers and, before I owned my own car, used to pick me up from home when we were working together. There was good camaraderie between the men. I recall he and I had a turn of duty for a week travelling to Salisbury Depot. On three consecutive nights we booked on to take out one of three 'W' class engines, Nos 31911, 31912 & 31922, each light engine. Every night we had to stop for steam because they were in such poor condition. The signalman must have wondered what had happened to us. When we finally got to Salisbury we left them there to be taken on to Exeter to be used for banking – how on earth they got on with them there I can only imagine.

On the other two nights, we travelled to Salisbury 'on the cushions'. Here a 'Q' had been prepared for us and we went to the yard to pick up a freight train for the return journey to Eastleigh. Coming out of Salisbury the gradient is on the steep side and with about 60 wagons on at 1 o'clock in the morning we made an awful lot of noise 'barking up the bank'. It was a lot easier once we reached level ground and the more favourable grades back to Eastleigh.

The Winchester shunter, 'B4' No 30096, attaching/detaching 'tail' traffic to a down train. A similar procedure applied to the watercress vans left here from Alresford. *Ian Shawyer collection*

A 1958 view of 'Lord Nelson' No 30853 *Sir Richard Grenville* passing under Bowker's footbridge near Shawford heading in the direction of Basingstoke. As a junior fireman Vernon fired one of these engines between Eastleigh and Basingstoke with the aid of a helpful driver. *Tony Molyneaux*

One of the terrible three 'W' class tank engines taken light to Salisbury. Even light engine it would not steam properly. This view was taken on 9 September 1961. *Tony Molyneaux*

The 'hurry up' job. A decidedly worn looking 'Terrier', No 32646 at Eastleigh on 18 April 1964. This was after the Hayling Island line had closed. *Tony Harris*

Another light engine story was during the time I was in the spare gang. One Sunday morning the Foreman came into the cabin and asked us to prepare two 'A1X' 'Terriers', Nos 32646 and 32678, for the Hayling Island branch as there were two crews coming up from Fratton to collect them after they had been serviced at Eastleigh. (Fratton was almost closed by then.) It was quite an experience to work on these little engines which subsequently went, coupled together, back to Fratton.

There were quite a few family members working on the railway, brothers like drivers Alec and Norman Bennett; Pete Bramble and his brother – their father was also a checker and used to check me in for work; fireman Norman Cox, his brother Les and one other brother, both drivers; Pete Bevan and his brother; Ikey Till and his nephew Nigel Till, and my own uncle, Archie Bennett who worked in the Railway Works. I remember too passed fireman Ron Jones who had come up from Exeter to become a driver at Eastleigh.

Other drivers and firemen that I remember, starting with the drivers: Hugh Abbinnett, Ray Allen, Ken Arnold, Dave Batten, Alec Bennett, Pete Bevan, Frank Campbell, Les Cox, E. Dale, Ron Dukes, Bill Fair, Ron Finch, Ken Frampton, Pete Francis, Harold Froud, Eddie Gates, Ron Hedges, Arthur Jones, Ron Light, Ben Livingstone, Bert Osborne, Roy Sloper, Jack Stevens, Arthur Taylor, Rodney Tizzard, Pete Windsor and George Wyatt. Firemen: Brian Alderman, Mike Alderman, Pete Brown, Ben Cartwright, Norman Cox, Tony Dawe, Malcolm Hall, Terry Hockey, Pete King, Zac Peel, John Smith, Martin Squibb, John Stubbington, Dave White and Len Witt.

I remember also booking on with my driver to prepare our engine, S15 No 30499, for a freight train from Bevois Park on the outskirts of Southampton to Feltham. The previous week, fireman Tony Dawes and his driver Pete Hickey had had the same engine which was a real disaster, dirty, blocked-up tubes, plus ash all over the brick arch which caused them to stop for steam four or five times even before they reached Basingstoke.

To find we had the same engine was a nightmare but we passed through Eastleigh looking OK and gave a confident wave to our mates in the cabin at the station – but only to get as far as Allbrook where we too ran out of steam. After recovery we struggled to Shawford Junction and built up enough steam to get to Wallers Ash where we again stopped, pausing once more at Worting Junction before finally limping into Basingstoke for the Feltham crew to take over. We wished them the very best of luck and handed the engine over with a huge sigh of relief – about 3 hours late! Another rough trip involved a local working with a 'U' and just three coaches, on this occasion we struggled to get to Micheldever and ran short of steam there.

This was not my last rough trip either. I recall signing on at the shed with driver Ben Livingstone, to work a passenger train to Basingstoke. We walked across to the station to await our train which came in with an 'N' class engine on the front and again just three coaches behind. As was usual the relieved crew exchanged details of the engine and admitted they were struggling for steam.

Empty stock working at Mount Pleasant near to Bevois Park, No 30484 heading north. *Tony Molyneaux*

Anyway off we went, only to get as far as Shawford just four miles on and stopped for steam. The next time we were forced to pause was at Wallers Ash where we were stuck for a good half-hour. I had to walk back to tell the guard what had happened with a few anxious passengers asking about the delay. When there was not enough steam, the brakes used to come on automatically so there was nothing to be done except wait. As soon as we had recovered we literally plodded on to Basingstoke where we got relief. To be fair that was near the end of steam and by then the engines were in a poor neglected state.

Several factors might be involved in why we could run out of steam especially towards the end. One was when the engines were not being maintained very well (if at all!), the men knowing they would be scrapped soon anyway. Having decent coal was another factor. Welsh coal was the best but this was not always available. An engine we took over could also have been on the road a long time with a dirty fire full of clinker meaning air could not get through the fire-bars. If the brick arch was also covered in ash the tube plate could become blocked. No heat going through the tubes, or a lesser number of tubes, meant less heat transfer to the water; result, less steam being produced and then not enough to maintain the schedule or as mentioned sometimes even enough to keep us going.

But there were good times too. One morning I booked on

and looked at my roster for the day – it was a special turn – with the engine rostered for the duty being No 30777, the last King Arthur class still in service. We were to take over the engine at Basingstoke, so my driver Alec and I travelled there on the cushions.

We reported to the foreman, only to be told that No 30777 had failed and we were instead given a West Country, No 34101. This engine had just come out of Eastleigh Loco works after being serviced, so was in pretty good condition. When the special arrived off the line from Reading, the Western engine came off and we backed on to take it forward to Bournemouth.

With the engine behaving well on the way down, passing through Micheldever and Wallers Ash, all downhill, the speedo told us that we were doing 100mph. No 34101 was certainly flying but she was also a bit rough at this speed especially for firing. By the time we passed through Winchester, a lot of the fire had shaken through the bars and I had to do a lot of firing to build up the fire again. Although it was hard work, it was also very enjoyable to reach that sort of speed by one's own efforts.

One night my driver and I took a freight train from Fareham to Gosport. We finished shunting about 3.0am and, after a cup of tea, fell asleep in the shunters' cabin. We woke up to find it was time to leave and the fire was almost out – what a panic to get it going again!

'U' class 'Mogul' No 31795 with the 6.15pm up stopper near Allbrook. Vernon had a couple of rough trips with these engines having to stop several times due to shortage of steam – to be fair this was when they were in run down condition. *Tony Molyneaux*

On a trip to Nine Elms freight yard with an original 'West Country' class, driver 'Wiggy' Bailey let me do the driving – quite a privilege then to a very young firemen but a lot of drivers were happy to swap places later on, preferring to fire the boat trains from Southampton to Waterloo while I drove the engine. One boat train I do recall was when we were diverted to take the Alton line instead of the more usual route through Basingstoke. This was an occasion when the main line was being re-laid ready for electrification.

A regular 'Mondays only' turn was to prepare the engine ('West Country' or 'Battle of Britain' usually) then take it, light engine, tender first to Southampton New Docks 101 berth. Here we coupled on to a boat train from one of the Cape boats which consisted of 8-10 passenger coaches and two bullion vans. Because of the cargo they carried, these vans were always marshalled next to the engine and were supposedly full of gold bullion bars mined in South Africa. On the journey to London, whenever the railway track passed close to a road, we always saw a police car, watching and waiting for us to pass safely by. There was also a big police and security presence at Waterloo when the train pulled in, ready to be unloaded. Some time later I had my own incident with the police. It appears the local post office at Swaythling was robbed by a villain wearing a grease top hat and who drove an Austin A40 –

similar to the one I had at the time. With the description put out, a well-meaning witness noticed me and my car as being similar. The police investigated and it was left to my mother to explain who I was, why I was dressed like that and where I was going at the time. On steam I would invariably come home with overalls covered in coal, oil and grease. Indeed, so bad were they on occasions that it was necessary to clean them outside using a bass broom.

When I was put in a spare gang, Alec Bennett was one of my regular drivers. We had a special turn with a Western engine, going to the Old Docks in Southampton to pick up a freight train and take it to Didcot via Basingstoke and Reading. Every box wagon was full of bananas from the big Fyffes warehouse in the docks. The Western engine had a water scoop and, never having used one before, Alec decided to try it out to take on water from the water troughs which ran between the tracks at Goring. We learnt later we should have only left the scoop down for a few seconds but Alec left it down for rather too long and before we knew it, we were flooded out whilst the overflow had caused most of the coal in the tender to be washed down on to the footplate with us. When we arrived in Didcot we were still sloshing about in water and coal dust. Our relief crew of Western men informed us where we had gone wrong but I think, by then, we knew!

No 34071 *601 Squadron* **at the Southampton Ocean Terminal.** *Tony Molyneaux*

Different generations of motive power at the rear of Eastleigh. A wonderful image dating from 7 October 1962. *Tony Molyneaux*

SW52 Next stop back to the depot for refuelling – we hop...! 12 October 1963. *Tony Harris*

On 12 October 1963, D6524 has just come off the DNS line at Shawford Junction with empty tank cars for Fawley. It was on one of these engines at Worthy Down that Vernon and his driver experienced a total failure. *Tony Molyneaux*

Again with Alec we booked on to work a different engine, a 9F, No 92211, tender first to Southampton Terminus which was also the first time I had ever fired a 9F. We had just three passenger coaches to couple up, which for a big engine like that was easy. We were booked to work all stations to Bournemouth and leave the engine there. Then after a meal break we had to prepare an engine, usually a 'West Country', at Bournemouth ready to work the up mail to Waterloo which arrived back at Southampton Terminus about 00.30. I recall we had the same duty and the same engine all week. Speaking of Bournemouth reminds me of another turn which was to work a 'West Country' to Bournemouth ready for it to do a run to Waterloo. Why Bournemouth should need one of these I could not work out as they, of course, had their own stud of these engines. Whatever the case, I am sure the roster clerks had their reasons. However, because of the voracious appetite for coal these engines had and the fact there was only a very short turn-around time at Bournemouth before it would be heading up to Waterloo with a train, we had to ensure there was enough coal for the round trip. Consequently the maximum amount of coal went on the tender and a similar amount in the firebox. Apparently this was the only way to ensure there was no shortage on the duty.

Occasionally, after we had unhooked at Southampton Terminus after midnight and the mail train had gone on its way to Waterloo with a different engine attached to the other end, the guard might ask if we would take a couple of members of the public with us on the footplate back to Eastleigh if they had missed the last train. We were booked to take the guard back with us anyway but add a few more bodies and it was often quite crowded on the footplate. Luckily we had enough steam to get us there without the need for shovelling coal.

I only experienced one derailment in my career. We picked up an 0-6-0 diesel shunter in Eastleigh yard to take back to the sheds for fuel. The foreman said we could go home after that, so, thinking we could get home early, we were in a hurry. However, the points weren't over properly and with a 'Bumpity Bump!' we were off the rails. No early finish now, for after having to fetch the breakdown crane and gang from the loco sheds we remained with the engine and by the time we were finished it was overtime.

As a fireman I also acted as a second man on the diesels. One of these turns involved being with Driver Bill Roberts on a goods to Newbury. Unfortunately we only got as far as Worthy Down as the engine expired and the turn was cancelled. I also spent time with some of the older men who were tasked with driving the DEMU sets. These units had a strong spring on the power controller and it took some effort to keep it depressed and so prevent the brakes coming on. A few disliked this arrangement intensely and so would sit back whilst I did the driving.

Speaking of diesels, I recall reading in 'SW44' mention of the Hymek type, class 35. This took me back to a time when four of us firemen had to go to Old Oak Common to learn how to operate the steam heat boilers on the class 47 Brush diesels.

These were used either on freight or the boat trains from Southampton to Waterloo, they were Nos D1921, D1922 & D1924. During the summer the boilers were not needed as they were purely for keeping the passengers warm.

I recall also I had a rostered job for the week during the winter. My driver Alec Bennett and I relieved a crew on a van train, 'West Country' No 34004, and took it to Basingstoke. Alec returned to Eastleigh on the cushions while the van train was taken on to Clapham by another crew. I remained at Basingstoke as I was booked to work with a Basingstoke driver. We met on the station platform to relieve the crew of the Hymek Diesel which was rostered on this turn.

'Hymek' D7089 at Eastleigh on 15 April 1967. Steam had less than three months left at this stage and Vernon was now in charge of the steam-heat boiler on these and the 'Brush Type 4' classes. *Tony Harris*

Eastleigh firemen were given this job as the men at Basingstoke had not received the training to operate the steam heat boilers. In essence it was similar to a car gear change to operate.

Having this turn for a whole week, I got to know the driver who also had the duty for the week. He would let me do the driving (while he took over my task of keeping an eye on the boiler). At Southampton Central I got relief from a Bournemouth fireman and my day's work was over.

Newly married in 1967 and living near St Denys station, if I was coming through St Denys on a light engine to the depot near the end of my shift, I would blow the whistle to let my wife know I had nearly finished and would be home soon.

Towards the end of the steam era Alec Bennett and I had a turn from Waterloo to Bournemouth with a lot of steam enthusiasts on board, going as far as Woking. Some of them came to the cab and asked Alec to blow the whistle and hammer the engine as hard as possible as they were filming the trip and wanted some good sound effects. Alec said 'We'll be all right for a good tip here,' and we duly obliged with a fast, furious and noisy journey to Woking, only for them all to disembark with a mere 'Thanks' over their shoulders as they walked away.

I was a spare man at Eastleigh on the last day of steam – a sad day as diesels and electrics took over but leaving me with happy memories of my own days- **'in steam'**.

Vernon remained on the railway for a further five years after the end of steam after which he would have had to transfer to Waterloo to continue his career commensurate with far longer working days. He decided against this and at the age of 26 left the railway to begin a 32 year career with the Ford Motor Company.

More in Colour from Graham Smith

Graham made several visits to the Island from 1959 onwards. Unfortunately there are no note-books or other records to confirm exact dates, etc, so unless otherwise stated the dates given are those when the slide was processed and which was at least the following month to when the view was taken. Here we see the Ryde Pierhead tramway at Pierhead waiting its next load of passengers to Esplanade. July 1968.

We are delighted to present another selection from the archives of Graham Smith, courtesy of Richard Sissons, and this time the selection made is from the Isle of Wight. In consequence of a previous offering one of our regulars, Richard Simmons, contacted us to mention he had worked with Graham in the offices at Waterloo. Graham apparently was a somewhat laid back character and who one afternoon happened to mention to Richard, 'I will be a bit late in tomorrow morning, something I want to see

on the way in.' With that Graham left Waterloo without informing Richard where he was bound. As luck would have it none other than the General Manager, Gordon Pettitt, came looking for Graham that same afternoon and on being told he had gone commented 'Get him to come and see me first thing in the morning.'

Knowing Richard was due to be late in the following day, Richard tried all he could to contact Graham at home but without success. The following morning he was told the GM wanted him and as this was not now the 'first thing' that had been demanded Richard expected potential fireworks. Graham however was unperturbed, duly went off to see the GM and emerged later still smiling. We shall never know what it was about!

A definite date on this occasion, 20 September 1959. No 29 *Alverstone* paused at Esplanade as the first stop on its way to Newport and Cowes. One of the tramway vehicles may just be seen on the left hand side at the far end of the canopy and just look at that wonderful long case clock under the awning.

No 27 *Merstone*, No 30 *Shorwell* and an unidentified third engine lined up at the running shed at Ryde St Johns on 17 February 1962. (The edge of the image just loses the second digit of the third engine.) Notice on the first engine there is a cover on the Westinghouse pump; the others being easier to 'clunk' with a spanner if persuasion is required to get the thing going again!

On the same day, No 14 *Fishbourne* is being attended to prior to service. The engine is a sparkling condition although perhaps the same cannot be said for the engineman's trousers.

This time it is a distinctly grubby No 29 *Alverstone* that is shunting a newly overhauled coach in July 1963. The missing signal arms applicable to the summer service may be noted.

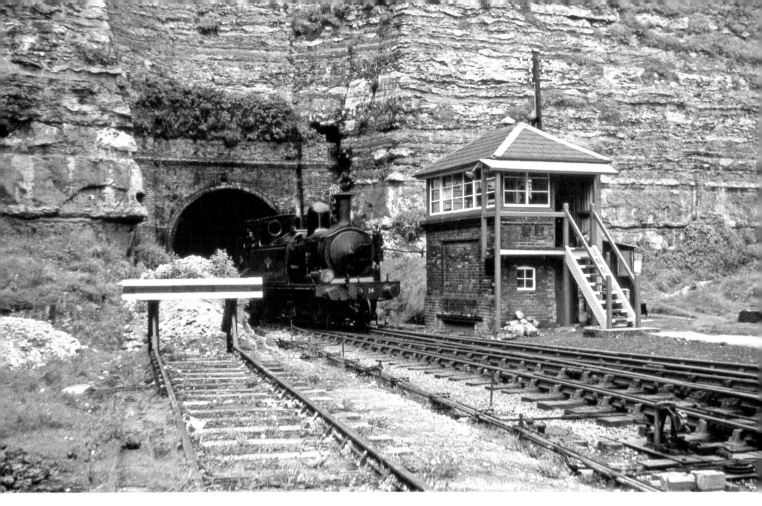

End of the line at Ventnor sometime in 1961. No 24 *Calbourne* is probably engaged in a shunt move – otherwise the signalman would likely be at the end of the veranda ready to take the tablet.

Summing up what the Island lines were really all about, a clean engine, No 14 *Fishbourne,* green coaches and a summer's day in 1964.

October 1964 at Ventnor. The well-known vista with its red telephone box, Southern Railway enamel signs and on this occasion it seems just two potential passengers. Plus contemporary road vehicles of course, left Ford Zephyr Mk2 and right a Morris Oxford type saloon.

Now taking the line to Cowes we first call at Havenstreet where No 17 *Seaview* crosses with what could be either No 20 or No 30. July 1963.

The new platform at Ashey recorded on 17 February 1962. Why there was felt to be a need for the station name to be shown at the rear of the platform is unknown.

A distinctly dirty No 17 *Seaview* on Newport viaduct in October 1964. The name of the firm 'Scats' was an acronym for the Southern Counties Agricultural Trading Co who were seed merchants and garden suppliers with branches throughout Hampshire – and at least one on the Island. They were active until taken over in recent times.

Cowes arrival: No 29 *Alverstone* on the last few yards of its journey into the terminus. After the passengers have exited the coaches will be pushed back towards Mill Hill, the engine released and then the vehicles gravity shunted back towards the buffers. At this time in June 1964 and notwithstanding the crowds that used the railway here during the summer months – see next image – the line had just two more summer seasons of operation as services here ceased in February 1966.

July 1963, the train has just arrived at Cowes and passengers are making their way, perhaps reluctantly, towards the exit and likely then down the hill to the ferry back to Southampton and a return to normal life. The sharp curvature of the station is apparent from the gap between the footboard and the platform.

No 28 *Ashey* in winter store at Sandown in March 1963. A light film of rust perhaps, and surprisingly no apparent cover for the chimney top. The nameplate is also still affixed.

S2450 clearly ex-works in October 1964 at Newport. This is a former SECR 54ft 1in birdcage brake third (mainland SR No 3367) to Diagram 158 and ran for many years at one end of 3-set 551 on South Eastern section 'rover' services. The set was augmented to about nine coaches later and renumbered 903, but in 1948/49 the three original coaches were rebuilt and transferred to the Isle of Wight, along with most of the other surviving ex-SECR 54ft 3-sets. The original configuration was a second class compartment, then a lavatory (the fourth window visible from the far end), then five third class compartments plus guard's van at the nearer end. The rebuilding – which dates from January 1949- replaced the guard's van with two more compartments (nearest) and altered the lavatory into a coupe (half-compartment) accessible from the adjacent third via a short side corridor. In this form, the coach was renumbered S2450 and arrived on the Island in April 1949. SR Diagram 40 was now allocated and the coach ran mostly as a loose strengthening vehicle until withdrawn in September 1966. Island coaches did not carry the 'S' suffix letter – if the coach was on the mainland, from 1951 it would have been lettered S2450S. The carriage code is slightly unusual – SC – presumably second coupe. For non-corridor stock this was normally shown just as 'S' – for second and only open seconds received the code 'SO' while corridor seconds received 'SK'. Note that much of the timber panelling has been replaced by plain steel-sheeting – including the upper end – where the birdcage lookout windows would formerly have been. Beyond is one of the seven 'utility' vans that went to the Island in 1950 – in steam days the most modern stock sent over. (With grateful thanks to Mike King.)

IOW interior saloon more akin to the drawing room than a railway carriage, July 1963. The actual vehicle is another rebuilt ex-SECR 54ft 1in coach – either second or first class – but probably the former in view of the brown colour of the upholstery and the lack of 'First class' window stickers. Eighteen of these were rebuilt from Diagram 313 composites between January 1948 and May 1949 but although they were all structurally identical they were fitted out differently by compartment. Island Diagrams 41, 376, 377, 378 and 378x were eventually allocated, depending on compartment trim. If a third (later second), as we think, then this is the interior of one of Diagram 41 coaches S2456/57/58, but the composites were numbered S6364/65/68-80. One almost feels that clouds of dust would rise if those cushions were beaten. (With grateful thanks to Mike King.)

January 1967 and No 22 *Brading*, shorn of its original nameplate and now displaying a smaller replacement, stands in Esplanade with an engineer's train during the temporary closure allied to electrification.

A Fishy Tale

Martin Burrell

'Betrayed by smell. Fish theft at Railway Station'.
(Taken from an unreported local newspaper of 1942.)

Said to have been given away by a 'fishy smell' on his hands. Richard George Proctor (soldier) was charged at Aldershot Police Court on Thursday with stealing 3½lbs of kippers, value 2s 11d, the property of the Southern Railway at Fleet on 24 January. He pleaded not guilty.

Benjamin Allen, a porter at Fleet Railway Station, stated that he was on duty shortly after 11pm on 24 January. A number of men came off a train, and he collected their tickets. After the train had passed him he heard laughing from the footbridge on the opposite platform. He went over, examined some boxes of kippers and saw that one was broken open and that some of the kippers were missing. He followed the men, overtook two soldiers in Fleet Road and reported to a constable whom he met. The constable went back but the men denied knowledge of the fish. It was noticed that the defendant wiped his hands on his coat and the constable smelt his hands and accused him of having taken the fish. The defendant admitted it and said he had thrown the kippers into a bush.

Police War Reservist Robinson stated that at 11.25pm on 24 January after receiving a report from the last witness, he went with Police War Reservist Squires towards Fleet Station where he saw the defendant and another soldier. When questioning the defendant he noticed that he rubbed his hands up and down inside his greatcoat pockets. He examined Proctor's hands which smelt very strongly of fish.

He denied knowledge of the fish alleged to have been stolen, but when asked to account for the smell of fish on his hands he said, 'When I was coming over the footbridge on the platform some chaps were arguing and they gave me something and I have just thrown a kipper over the hedge.' The witness went to the spot the defendant indicated and found three kippers. The following morning he went to the same spot and found six more kippers.

The defendant in evidence stated that he met a friend at the station. They walked up Fleet Road, came up with a gang of soldiers who gave him something which he took in his hand. He saw the gang throw something over a hedge and run through a gate so he threw away what he had.

In cross-examination the defendant said the kippers were not wrapped, and he did not know what they were when first put into his hand.

The Magistrates found the case proved. The defendant was given a very good military character, and the magistrates dismissed the summons on payment of 21s costs, the chairman telling him he had acted in a silly manner. 'We think you were skylarking more than anything else' he said.

(Martin kindly submitted this piece in consequence of looking through some more paperwork from his late relative, former Waterloo Station Master Joseph (Jock) Callaghan. See 'SW47'.)

Fleet – the one that almost got away. Now we know why stations so often smelt of fish, I had always thought it was some form of disinfectant!
J. Eyers/South Western Circle collection

Down to Earth Part 2
Mostly Ex-LSWR Coaches
Mike King

This picture originally appeared in the *South Western Magazine* in the early 20th Century hence its somewhat grainy appearance. It is a former 3-compartment 19ft 6in first of 1859 grounded as a sports pavilion at Barnes Cricket Club by the LSWR themselves – probably somewhere near the station at Barnes Common. This is unlikely therefore to be the current Barnes Cricket Club who have played at their Lonsdale Road ground since 1919 but more likely the site at Vine Road which is adjacent to the railway. The last of these coaches (24 in number) was withdrawn in 1900 so this gives an idea of the date of grounding. Note that the coach body sits on a properly prepared base complete with brick edging. Only the right-hand compartment door remains in use – the others have been permanently sealed up. The board along the roof advertising the club is believed to have been red, with white letters shaded black but the overall colour of the body is unknown – cricket white maybe? Just how long it remained there is unknown. *South Western Magazine*

In Part 1, we looked at grounded goods wagons – mostly vans. Now we shall turn our attention to passenger coaches that were grounded or sold off for private use. Whereas goods vehicles mostly only lent themselves to being used as storage huts, carriage bodies could also be used as office accommodation or built into dwellings – the former usually (but not always) by the railway companies themselves, the latter by private individuals or occasionally by private companies for their own office accommodation. Indeed, a visitor to the

shingle wasteland that is Dungeness, Kent, even today would find a number of grounded carriage bodies still being used as homes – albeit mostly covered by ship-lap timber and roofing felt or incorporated into larger structures, however a visit by the late Roger Kidner in the 1930s revealed a great many more – some still visibly carrying their former numbers and company insignia. Even in August 1949, the late Denis Cullum listed no less than 38 bodies but he could only positively identify 8 of them. By 1978, the number was down below 30, none of which visibly displayed their former identities and some of these were almost unrecognisable as railway vehicles.

We will begin with ex-LSWR stock. The fact that Dungeness held LSWR, LBSCR and SECR vehicles points to the likelihood that most groundings at this location date from after 1923 – although some of the South Eastern bodies may have arrived from Ashford Works prior to the Grouping. Most pre-1923 sold-off LSWR coaches tended to be found within South Western territory – as it clearly made sense, if you wanted such a structure, to approach your local company. However, we will also look at ex-Somerset & Dorset Joint Railway stock and a small number of these were sold off – prior to about 1930 presumably from Highbridge Works but by the location of several others, latterly more likely from Lancing. Most South Western vehicle sales originated from Eastleigh – and LSWR carriage register entries give such details as 'To Carr. Dept. Woking' or 'To shunter's cabin, Amesbury' and 'Sold 4/17, Winchester Gas Company,' to name but three. Unfortunately, SR registers usually confine their details to the simple entry 'B/S' or 'Body sold,' with a date – but seldom are further location details given. Such details (or more likely the name of the purchaser) were usually noted in the minutes of the Carriage & Wagon Committee meetings, together with the revenue accrued from the sales, but rarely were carriage numbers quoted in these minutes.

Some of the oldest vehicles to survive date from as early as the 1850s – the *South Western Magazine* once published a photograph of a 19ft 6in long 3-compartment first of 1859, doing duty as Barnes Cricket Pavilion and reproduced herewith. Similarly the *Railway Magazine* for November 1904 featured a picture of an identical body on the track side near Waterloo – so there was clearly already some interest in these ancient survivors, which even then looked very different to what was actually running on the railway. A few of this vintage survived to the 1960s – there was an ancient body alongside Bournemouth West station platforms but it had long been tarred over and any trace of the former number was long gone. The body did, however, yield information about early LSWR paint colours and details of these may be found in the HMRS *LSWR Livery Register*. Another early carriage body could be found on the down platform at Swaythling station – and this was another use found for them; either as a goods warehouse or occasionally as a passenger waiting room at some out-of-the-way station. The independent light railway empire of Colonel Holman F. Stephens would specialise in these – as they were cheap to buy!

The *South Western Railway Magazine* for October 1922 carried an article entitled 'Old Carriage Bodies For Sale' – so clearly this was an advertisement for the service and the fact that they had an excess of bodies for disposal following World War 1. The article was illustrated by a 30ft 5-compartment third class coach – almost certainly the most numerous ex-LSWR design to be grounded – but also included two interior views showing a coach body converted into a bedroom and a living room. The price stated was £20 per coach body, delivered to your local station. The article concluded with a picture of an LSWR goods van body of 1881 vintage – serving as a butcher's shop at Byfleet, so there was another, if only occasional, use for them.

Bogie vehicles began to be grounded by the 1930s – indeed, there were just two such coaches at Dungeness (both ex-LSWR saloons) but groundings of these tended to be much more common adjacent to the railway – moving them to locations distant from a running line was clearly more difficult – but it did happen. Four- and six-wheeled coaches were most definitely the more numerous and preferred for conversion into dwellings. However, it could simply be that most sales occurred at a period when these coaches were being scrapped and by the time bogie vehicle bodies were available, greater affluence prevailed. When first researching the subject, one aspect that

the writer was not expecting was to find the same coach body in different places. A few did actually get moved about – albeit mostly the smaller bodies and usually by only a few yards, but very occasionally a bogie coach got shifted to a completely different location. This seemed most common during the war or just after – probably reflecting rapidly changing needs and the general shortage of alternative buildings.

Come wartime and things entered a very different scenario. There was suddenly a need for additional accommodation – both offices and storage – in case more permanent locations were damaged by bombing – and many of these might be needed at extremely short notice. Groundings soon rapidly increased in number – mostly adjacent to the railway, but the needs of the Army and Government departments also had an effect. At certain strategic and country locations, various depots were set up – there was a Home Guard depot south of Gomshall that held over half a dozen coach bodies from 1942 onwards. A complete 3-coach corridor set (No 405, comprising brake thirds 3094 and 3112, plus composite 5095, found themselves here, along with six other vehicles – all of which feature in the New Cross Gate foreman painter's list mentioned last time. The years of austerity following the war also ensured that groundings continued – sometimes a newer body replacing an older one – but as the 1960s approached it was obvious that the days of the grounded body were numbered and many on railway land began to be demolished as rationalisation and closures gathered pace.

Grounded corridor coaches were more uncommon – general withdrawal of such ex-LSWR vehicles started about 1945 so the set at Gomshall was an early disposal. Another location with a collection of such structures could be found at Wembley Hill, Middlesex – where by 1948 a dozen were collected together on a trading estate – owned by Messrs Johnson Matthey Ltd – and this was duly visited by enthusiast Denis Cullum, but how he had found out about it in the first place I do not know. Another complete 3-coach corridor set was grounded here, together with two former LSWR restaurant cars plus a selection of LBSCR and SECR vehicles, and two District Railway coaches. While mentioning the Underground, it is worth noting that the two Metropolitan Railway Pullmans *Mayflower* and *Galatea* were grounded at Hinchley Wood in late 1939 – at a builders merchant near the station. Whilst the writer cannot prove it, he believes this was at the premises of Messrs Hall & Company but they were certainly gone by the 1960s and the builder's yard had by then

been modernised. It still functions today but in the ownership of Jewsons. Other early Pullmans were also grounded – as we will see when looking at former LBSCR stock.

Perhaps the most unusual ex-LSWR grounding was of the carriage body section of Drummond's 'bug' – the F9 class 4-2-4 tank inspection saloon which the great man used as his personal transport around the South Western – checking up on everything and everybody! After the Grouping this was used for conducted tours of Southampton Docks during the early 1930s but was then stored at Eastleigh until wartime. The chassis became a boiler trolley around the works, while the body was grounded as Mr Pepper's office – as illustrated in SW 50.

We will now look at a selection of vehicles – wherever possible giving their histories and the dates at which they finally disappeared, if known. As before – if you wish to search out those that remain, please ensure you obtain permission from the owner before trespassing on what may be somebody's home or on private land.

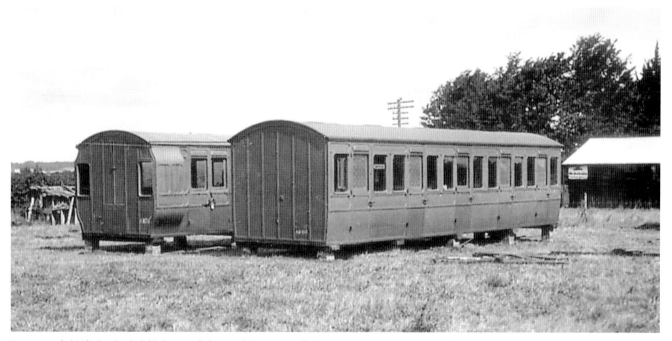

Two arc-roofed 30ft six-wheeled thirds grounded at Wool in 1923 – easily the most numerous type of LSWR coach to be grounded. In excess of 120 were built between 1883 and 1892 – some as second class but most as thirds – with a number subsequently being rebuilt as brake thirds (including the coach on the left) and most were withdrawn from passenger traffic between 1907 and 1926. At least 65 were either grounded by the railway, sold to the War Department or sold off privately between 1917 and 1924. Locations noted in the registers are as diverse as Tresmeer, Selsey, Swanage, Wareham, Woking and Andover, while at least six (LSWR Nos 280, 692, 709, 807, 830 and 858) were consigned to Wool, but it has not proved possible to identify this pair further. Several became fruit vans in their final days – with their seating removed and shelving provided on which to load the fruit packing cases – and these were the last survivors, some remaining in seasonal use until 1930, in LSWR livery to the end. Both coaches in the picture were purchased by Mr A. Tranter on 4 August 1923, for the sum of £39. The price included eight second-hand headstocks that were used to sit the bodies upon. Note the reduction in price of at least one pound in recognition of the fact that two bodies were consigned to the same location at the same time! They were manoeuvred into position by a local farmer – spaced some eight feet apart to enable a further living area to be constructed beneath a trussed timber roof that would span above and between the two bodies. Construction of this took place during 1925 and the completed property – named 'The Folly' – became a holiday bungalow for the next 80 years. Starting in 2007 the structure has been completely rebuilt on a concrete base, but retaining the two carriage bodies, repainted in 2011 in LSWR salmon and brown livery, and has since been available as a holiday let. As such, it has featured in the magazine *Dorset Life* for March 2019. Regrettably, at the time of writing, all such holiday lets have had to cease. A much longer article about the coaches appeared in the *South Western Circular* for April 2012. I am grateful to the present owners David and Alison Saunders for much additional information and a number of photographs.

Above: **At Padstow there were six carriage bodies on the quayside and most were used by Messrs Pawlyn Brothers who had a fish-curing factory adjacent. In this 1948 picture we see three of them – all ex-LSWR six-wheelers, but further to the right was a former Brighton third class coach. Nearest is 34ft former composite LSWR No 386, built in 1884. This was ciphered (i.e. placed on the duplicate list with a zero in front of the running number) as No 0386 in June 1910 and was probably used for troop movement during the First World War. In 1919 it was converted into a brake composite with the far end third class compartment altered to a guard's van, being renumbered yet again as No OA2. This curious alpha numeric numbering was used by the South Western during and after World War 1 for coaches already on the duplicate list that changed class – there were OE and OV prefixed numbers as well. In neither instance were such coaches expected to survive for very long, but events here would prove otherwise! After the Grouping the coach was yet again re-classified to brake first as SR duplicate No 0802, this taking place at Ashford Works on 20 May 1924 and it was then formed at one end of duplicate set No 029 along with identical brake first No 0803, five other LSWR arc-roofed third class coaches and four ex-SER 4-wheelers, to be used as a stop-gap on commuter, workmen's or hop-pickers' trains on the South Eastern section. Remarkably this was not the end, as in February 1927 it was renumbered yet again as SR No 7718 and became part of first class race train set No 347, along with its twin No 0803, which was renumbered SR No 7719. Eight six-wheeled LSWR firsts were marshalled in between the brake coaches and the set was used for race train specials to such locations as Ascot and Epsom on a few days each year until final withdrawal on 30 September 1930 – gas-lit to the end. Not that this would have bothered the passengers very much, as most of the popular horse-racing meetings were held during the summertime. One might think that scrapping would rapidly take place, but the coach was then grounded at Padstow where it remained until about 1964. Behind it may be seen two of the other LSWR grounded firsts that also formed part of SR race train sets Nos 345, 346 or 347 – these being 32ft 6in firsts Nos 7011/12 and 32ft lavatory firsts Nos 7690/92 – all dating from the 1880s and grounded in 1930.** *J. H. Aston*

Below and right: **As if this wasn't enough, companion coach No 0803/7719 was also grounded – but this time built into a bungalow at Middleton-on-Sea in 1930. The site was redeveloped in late 2016 and the coach was acquired by the MidHants Railway and is now probably in store at Eastleigh – awaiting restoration and provision of a suitable underframe on which to mount it – along with four ex-LBSCR coach bodies recovered some years earlier from Hayling Island. The history of this vehicle is identical to SR No 7718 – starting life as LSWR No 390 in 1885, then No 0390 and No OA1 from 1919. It joined coach No 0802/7718 in SR duplicate set No 029 and finally at the other end of race train set No 347 until September 1930 before being grounded many miles from its companion. In the main picture the two windows put into the brake end may be seen, while the inset shows the former identity and faded SR livery. One may also see the remains of white-painted render that had covered much of the coach side in recent years. This was a not uncommon addition to many grounded bodies in an attempt to improve thermal comfort and weatherproofing, especially at seaside locations. The new brick bungalow seen behind is visible proof why such wooden structures are no longer desirable.** *Photographer unknown*

The LSWR built a small number of semi-elliptical roofed six-wheelers between 1895 and 1904 and most of these ran in 'block' suburban sets until the early 1930s – latterly as nine-coach formations for workmen's trains but used at weekends for excursion traffic. Most were withdrawn between 1930 and 1933. This is a 32ft long 3-compartment brake third to SR Diagram 103 grounded on a farm at Gay Street, between Pulborough and West Chiltington, soon after withdrawal. Its exact identity remains unknown but was probably one of SR Nos 2601/7-12/15/18-23. The photograph dates from 1955. A similar 34ft 6-compartment third, SR No 44, was grounded at nearby Thakeham and was discovered by the writer as recently as 1988, still clearly exhibiting its SR livery, number and lettering. *D. Cullum*

A few ex-Somerset & Dorset Joint Railway six-wheelers were also grounded during the 1920s and 1930s. This is 31ft long 5-compartment third No 125 grounded as a store at Branksome loco shed, perhaps sometime in the 1920s – but certainly before the division of the joint line's carriage stock between the Southern and the LMS in 1930, as it fails to appear in that inventory and it clearly retains blue livery and the S.&D.J.R. garter crest. Built in 1885 by The Oldbury Carriage & Wagon Company of Birmingham, it was one of at least 16 constructed during the mid-1880s by that concern. A further 20 similar coaches built later either at Highbridge Works or by Cravens Ltd survived to become SR stock in 1930 and were allocated to SR Diagrams 93 or 95 (the reason why the difference is not known). A few received SR livery and numbers but all had been withdrawn by late 1932. S.& D.J.R. Nos 98 and 114 were of this type (built respectively by Cravens and the S.& D.J.R. at Highbridge Works) and became SR Nos 1419 and 1423 in 1930, later being sold off and built into bungalows near Chichester. Both were recovered in the 1990s by the Somerset & Dorset Trust and are now in the process of being restored at Washford. How long the coach at Branksome lasted is unknown. *L & GRP*

At least two more ex-Somerset & Dorset coaches were sold off from Lancing Works in 1932 and became bungalows at Pagham. This is 31ft brake third No 84, another coach built by Cravens in 1891, which became SR No 2787 in 1930 and ran at one end of SR set No 704 until withdrawn on 8 October 1932. SR Diagram 224 or 226 was allocated, but again the differences between the two are not known. The picture was taken on 6 September 1949 and the coach has clearly been incorporated into a larger structure with an overall roof that spans a living space between this and another coach situated a few feet behind. Note also the bow window at the end! Some coach bodies remain here today, but nothing like as many as when the writer first visited in 1967 and most are now almost unrecognisable. *D. Cullum*

A somewhat more exotic ex-Somerset & Dorset coach, also seen on 6 September 1949 at Pagham beach. This is a 31ft former saloon, either S.& D.J.R. No 89 or 108, built respectively at Highbridge in 1887 and 1891. Both came to the Southern in 1930 to be renumbered Nos 7999/8000 and also ran in SR set No 704. Both were built as first class saloons but were downgraded to 'picnic' saloon thirds in 1928, with 32 seats. The narrow window to the right was formerly the lavatory. SR Diagram 647 was allocated. Incidentally, these were the highest numbers allocated to SR steam-hauled coaches – numbers from 8001 upwards were reserved for electric stock. Like brake third No 2787, both saloons were withdrawn on 8 October 1932 and both are accurately recorded in SR registers as being sold off. Architecturally, the building into which this vehicle has been incorporated looks similar to the previous picture, even if construction materials differ. Saloon coaches were often a popular choice for building into houses, as they were usually open internally and featured large windows such as seen here. *D. Cullum*

Ex-LSWR grounded bogie coaches were never as numerous as six-wheelers. These are two early arc-roofed examples, seen at Newport, Isle of Wight, in the 1950s. The visible coach was former 46ft composite No 6385, withdrawn in September 1942. This was built by Birmingham RCW Co in 1884 as LSWR No 364, later renumbered as No 2584. It was at first allocated SR mainland number 5101 and was sent to the Island in July 1923, being renumbered as No 6385 in August 1931, running as the centre coach in 3-set 490. The other coach, whose end only may be seen, was former brake third No 4141 and the history of this coach is similar to No 6385. See next picture. *Alan Blackburn*

Sister-coach to brake third No 4141, this is coach No 4139 but grounded at Newhaven in 1941, having been repatriated to the mainland following Isle of Wight service. This was unusual, but not unknown and seven of the nine ex-LSWR arc-roofed bogie coaches sent to the Island were returned to the mainland for disposal during 1939. It is also worth noting that several coach bodies grounded at Hayling Island were also formerly running on the Isle of Wight. Built as a 48ft brake composite in June 1891, with six passenger compartments, two lavatories and a small guard's van in the centre of the coach, numbered LSWR 437 and later 3526, it was altered to a brake third in 1923 with the lavatories and one first class compartment removed, forming an enlarged guard's van in their place. In this form and to SR Diagram 133, it and three others were shipped to the Isle of Wight – this taking place in July 1923 – taking SR brake third number 3151. In 1931 it was again rebuilt, with two extra compartments put into the guard's van (to the right of the lookout), when it was renumbered 4139 and re-allocated to SR diagram 133A. Of the four Island transfers, only coach No 4140 was not rebuilt in 1931. Coach No 4139 also ran in Island 3-set 490 until withdrawn in April 1939. The New Cross Gate foreman painter's list advises that the coach was prepared for grounding at Newhaven Town yard in January 1941, where it remained until at least the mid-1950s. The photograph was taken in June 1947. This location (together with Newhaven Harbour) held at least 16 grounded bodies – including, by the mid-1960s, a rare grounding of a Maunsell 'Thanet' composite coach (No 5542). *D. Cullum*

The more modern-looking semi-elliptical roof profile was adopted by the LSWR in 1893 and many short (between 42ft and 51ft) non-corridor coaches were built from then into the early 20th Century. This is a 48ft 4-compartment brake third dating from 1896 – LSWR No 1137 and later No 1977. It was originally built with five passenger compartments but during 1923 the guard's van was enlarged and the double doors to the right of the lookout were added. In this form, it was allocated SR Diagram 112 and SR number 2663 and ran at one end of 4½ set No 294 (so-called because it was formed of four bogie coaches and a 6-wheeled van) on South Western section local services until about 1934. It was then transferred to 'long' set 930 – a 10-coach formation of LSWR short non-corridors on South Eastern section excursion trains until officially withdrawn in December 1938. However, the coach remained in some sort of passenger service as a loose vehicle until 1940, when it was finally prepared for grounding beside Eastleigh loco shed, where it is seen in August 1946, by now looking rather tatty. The New Cross Gate painter's list gives the date of grounding as February 1940. Not surprisingly the environs of Eastleigh shed, locomotive and carriage works, plus the surrounding yards, gave plenty of scope for grounded bodies and more than 50 are recorded at these locations. In later years (1970s and 1980s) some SR utility vans were grounded as replacements for earlier structures. *D. Cullum*

One of just two bogie coaches to be grounded at Dungeness, this LSWR saloon sits opposite *The Britannia* public house. It remains there today, but is now clad in ship-lap timbers so looks far less like a railway coach. Photographed in August 1949, it then went under the name 'Windwhistle' – highly appropriate for the location, it must be said! Today, it goes under a different name. There is some doubt about its former identity, but it was a 47ft 6in saloon coach built originally by Birmingham RCW Co in 1885, as an arc-roofed saloon first – one of six – and four were later rebuilt with a semi-elliptical roof profile. At the far end was a fairly conventional second class compartment – perhaps for domestic staff, followed by a large first-class saloon having three large windows, a centrally-placed lavatory, another first-class saloon, with a luggage compartment at the nearer end, accessed by double doors. In this form it would have provided accommodation for a family, plus servants and luggage, going to or from holiday or the like. SR coach numbers of the four were Nos 7806/7 and Nos 7933/34 and this might be any one of them. All were withdrawn in 1931-33, giving some idea of their arrival date at Dungeness. A very similar colour picture of the coach appears on page 25 of my *Southern Vans & Coaches in Colour* album (Noodle Books, 2015 – but still available from Crecy Publishing), taken in 1973.

Now for a small anecdote about saloons: While inspecting some of the coaches being used as living accommodation, the writer has engaged in conversation with the owners. In many instances, they were keen to impart their knowledge of the coach in question. Sometimes this was accurate, sometimes not. In the case of saloon vehicles, invariably the story went that the coach was a former Royal, used by Queen Victoria. Diplomacy was sometimes needed and the story went uncorrected, but rarely was this likely to be true. However, always be prepared for the unexpected… . At a model railway exhibition in Southampton Civic Centre in the mid-1980s, a gentleman closely scrutinised my then recent drawing of the LSWR Royal saloon. He told me that the clerestory on the roof as I had drawn it was too small. He knew this because he lived nextdoor to the coach and suggested that I made a visit to West Chiltington to see it. He was absolutely correct on both counts and I had to revise my drawing!! The coach body was later offered for sale to the Bluebell Railway – they declined it but did take the ex-LBSCR first that was with it. The LSWR saloon (LSWR No 17 and later SR No 7805) did eventually find a buyer and in 2017 featured in a Channel Four TV programme about its restoration. *D. Cullum*

Even the most unusual coaches might be grounded. This is LSWR 'gate' stock 50ft trailer brake composite No 6556 grounded as a mess room at Newhaven loco shed and seen in May 1949. There were 31 'gate' coaches with eight ultimately destroyed by enemy action (at Weymouth) while a further eight were grounded at various locations between 1939 and 1941. The most numerous type was this – to SR Diagram 415 – with 12 examples. They ran as six 2-coach pull-push sets between 1919, when they were rebuilt from Dugald Drummond's unsuccessful steam rail motors until the rather unreliable LSWR 3-wire P-P apparatus was replaced by the rather better ex-LBSCR air-control system in 1930/31. Most of the coaches were not re-equipped with the later equipment and then often ran as loose vehicles for the remainder of their lives. Coach No 6556 began life as H13 class rail motor No 3 in 1905, being rebuilt as brake composite No 4314 about July 1919, being paired soon after with similar coach LSWR No 4315 as pull-push set 19, later renumbered as coaches Nos 6556/57 and SR pull-push set No 366. During that time the set was noted on both the Bentley-Bordon branch and working between Torrington and Halwill Junction, usually paired but sometimes as single vehicles. The pair were permanently split up after 1931 and coach No 6556 alone of all the Diagram 415 vehicles was then equipped with air control pull-push apparatus, which it retained until withdrawal in December 1939, however it is not known where it was employed during this period. After withdrawal it was grounded as seen, according to the New Cross Gate workshops foreman painter's list, in January 1940. By the look of its condition, it probably did not last for long after being photographed. The final trailer brake composites in ordinary service ran on the Callington branch until 1956 – these were coaches Nos 6557/58 but they were outlasted by two other 56ft 'gate' pull-push sets. *D. Cullum*

Opposite page: Few later 56ft LSWR coaches were grounded – probably for two reasons. Firstly, they were getting cumbersome to move around and, secondly, withdrawals did not gain momentum until the late 1940s, by which time the need for such groundings was beginning to diminish. The writer is only aware of these two vehicles, both grounded together within Ashford Wagon Works sometime in the early 1950s. Neither are their identities known – despite much scraping of the paintwork at locations likely to reveal the old numbers!! Both were photographed in September 1974. The first picture shows a Diagram 17 lavatory third (SR numbers 604-642) – one of 39 built between 1904 and 1910 and these ran as one of the centre coaches in 4-coach cross-country sets numbered between 130 and 151, 251-263 and 311-314 until the late 1930s, when the sets were reduced to just three coaches and the Diagram 17 vehicles then became loose stock until withdrawn between 1944 and 1957. The other picture shows a Diagram 125 brake third – the variety with two pairs of sliding luggage doors – and these ran at each end of 4-coach (later 3-coach) sets Nos 101-121 and 159-162. A total of 50 were built in 1910/11 (SR nos 2999-3048) and withdrawals also encompassed the years 1944-57. *Author*

Similarly, few LSWR corridor coaches were grounded. Apart from the two complete 3-coach sets mentioned in the text, just a couple of composite coaches were grounded – at Woking and Lancing. This is Diagram 279 coach SR No 5097 at Lancing in June 1950 – still exhibiting its full Southern livery and lettering. Built in 1910 as LSWR No 1000, later 3102, it ran until September 1949, after which the coach gave up its underframe for inspection saloon No DS1 (suitably shortened for the purpose) and the body came to rest within Lancing yard. It was previously noted in SR corridor sets Nos 309 and 420. Just behind to the right may be seen the body of LBSCR 'Balloon' composite No 6282, while new Bulleid stock occupies the lines in the far background. *D. Cullum*

Opposite top: Former guard's and luggage vans were often chosen as grounded bodies – being open internally they required little stripping before being suitable for their new role. These ancient arc-roofed 30ft vans with a central raised lookout date from 1882-85 and over 120 were built. Several were sold to the Army during World War 1 and others entered departmental service or were grounded from about 1910 onwards. Examples are known to have been grounded at Okehampton and Wadebridge loco sheds. This particular van became LSWR departmental 75s as part of the Eastleigh breakdown crane set before 1923 and was renumbered SR 048s (the number is visible in the door panel) after 1923. It was withdrawn in October 1940 and grounded at Eastleigh Works, where it is seen in 1947. The former LSWR running numbers are unknown. A small number of these vans remained in service at Grouping and were allocated SR van numbers 16-22 but few were ever repainted or renumbered into SR livery. *F. Foote*

Bottom: Few ex-LSWR bogie luggage vans were grounded. This is an example of SR Diagram 863 – a 44ft guards van and one of at least 160 completed between 1893 and 1902. They were the South Western's most numerous passenger guard's vans and all except nine became SR stock; numbered in the van list between SR 149 and 309. Sixteen were converted into ambulance cars during World War 1 and most returned to the LSWR with gangway connections and electric lighting fitted – becoming SR Diagram No 864 after the Grouping. Withdrawal spanned 1926 until 1939 but several were sent to the Isle of Wight and lasted to 1956. The identity of this grounded van seen at Andover Junction in June 1951 is not known, but others are known to have been grounded at Lancing, Nine Elms, Eardley Road, Wimbledon and Exmouth Junction. *P. E. Barnes*

A 24ft ventilated luggage van, SR No 1291, seen at Beach Road, Winchelsea, on 22 August 1949 and one of 16 bodies noted by the photographer at that location. This was to SR Diagram 927 and was built in 1897 as LSWR luggage van No 101, later 5101. There were 135 of these and they were allocated SR numbers 1291-1424/27 after the Grouping but there were at least three variations in panelling detail. Van No 1291 was grounded in 1936 and still retains SR livery some 13 years later. An elevated 'pillbox' – part of the World War 2 beach defences – may be seen behind. *D. Cullum*

Opposite top: The later type of LSWR 24ft luggage van with sliding doors is represented by SR No 1451, seen at Tisbury in 1968. This was to SR Diagram 929 and is typical of 204 vans built from 1909-1923, SR numbers being Nos 1428-1611/13-32 – the last twenty built just after the Grouping. This particular van was LSWR No 5025 and dates from September 1917. It became a store for Messrs Wakefields Ltd at Tisbury in late 1939 and retained its wheels and under gear, but was not actually on the rails – one of a small number of vehicles similarly 'grounded'. It was later used by agricultural firm S.C.A.T.S. and remained on site until 1970 when it was then sold into preservation and has now been fully restored to LSWR livery at the Buckinghamshire Railway Centre at Quainton Road. A similar van awaits restoration on the Bluebell Railway. *A. E. West*

Bottom: Similar Diagram 929 van SR No 1597 converted to a cycle shelter and seen at Fratton loco shed in April 1950. The centre section of bodywork (between the two pillars) has been removed to make access easier. The photographer noted that it was still in green livery when photographed. Built as LSWR No 5511 in February 1921, it was grounded in March 1941 and lasted until Fratton shed ceased to be used for regular steam locomotive servicing in about 1964. *J. L. Smith*

A somewhat older arc-roofed LSWR 24ft passenger luggage van, grounded on a farm near Holsworthy in Devon, seen in the early 1960s. It is thought to be LSWR No 64, later 5064, built in June 1887 and sold as long ago as February 1923 – possibly as a result of the article in the *South Western Magazine* a few months earlier. Two others were sold off at about the same time – LSWR records stating that they went to Basingstoke and Horsebridge. There were fifty such vans, all built at Nine Elms Works in 1887 and 39 survived at the Grouping to be allocated SR Diagram 926 and traffic department numbers 1252-90 although many were never renumbered or repainted in SR livery before withdrawal. No 5064 failed to be allocated a Southern number and was clearly withdrawn just before the renumbering scheme was worked out, but sister-vans Nos 5063/65 were scheduled to become SR Nos 1262 and 1263. In the event, neither did so – van No 5063 instead becoming departmental No 083s in September 1925, while No 5065 was withdrawn in January 1926, still in LSWR livery. Three vans were sent to the Isle of Wight in 1926 and were the last survivors in railway service, running until 1936/37 and outlasting the final mainland examples by four years.

Next time, ex-LBSCR stock Part 1.

By Bulleid to Waterloo or 'Bulleid Woes'

John Newton

No 34064 *Fighter Command* **(with or without the Giesl is not confirmed) at speed and with definite evidence of a casing fire**. *Roger Thornton*

This is a tale of fact based on uncertainty, just like the 'star'(?), one of Bulleid's brilliant but controversial pacifics. There isn't even any certainty about the identity of the main characters, a 'Merchant Navy' and a 'Light Pacific' (let alone whether West Country or Battle of Britain), and a '700' 0-6-0 or possibly something still older. The story is true but the facts are more than a little blurred by the passing of over 50 years, with no written account made or photos taken at the time. I did possess a camera but couldn't afford to spend a student grant on railway photos; now how I wish I had indeed thrown caution to the wind and let rip on all those loco types which I must have seen in the Exeter area but do not remember now – instead of buying food and text books for my studies. Foolish indeed.

To start with even the date is uncertain. It was possibly the start of the summer term, 1967 at the college in London, which I was attending at the time, but, considering that 0-6-0, must surely have been earlier. More of that later. What I do know is that it was a glorious day and I had been enjoying my journey from Exeter, probably on the up ACE, particularly as I had managed to get a compartment to myself so I could peer out of the window, without restraint, to my heart's content.

The trip had been uneventful until we reached Worting Junction from where I was looking forward to a glorious gallop along the up Fast to Waterloo, no hold ups being anticipated. But it was not to be. After a while on went the brakes and it soon became apparent this was not just a preceding service holding us back but a serious stop. Which we duly did. Then nothing. I don't remember just how long we waited nor the exact order of events but after a while an ancient, and to a West Country man, a very foreign-looking, black 0-6-0 trundled by on the up slow (actually it passed quite nippily). Quiet descended again, our pacific just simmering in the early summer heat haze. I was near the front, it being my favoured place in the train, and I can remember occasional noises from the loco crew as they calmed their beast. Her safety valves must have lifted with all that pent up energy going to waste but I don't remember.

After perhaps 10 minutes an electric passed, also on the 'slow', but didn't stop. What HAD happened that affected only the 'fast' line? A pregnant pause (poetic licence) and another electric arrived and stopped beside us. That restored one's feeling of 'Express' superiority. At least both tracks were affected. I think it was at this point that, unencumbered by the presence of disapproving fellow passengers, I ventured into the empty guard's compartment next to mine. Remember it was a west country express, consequently complete with numerous brake thirds from the 'Withered Arm'. What I had in mind was to try out the effectiveness of those periscopes with little seats that the guards had for viewing the line ahead. It didn't disappoint, I had a clear view of the magnificent gantry of compressed air signals ahead, all firmly at 'ON'.

Another long wait, it was very hot in the sun now, probably about an hour all told. Then -movement. We started forward, not with any great enthusiasm, but at least we left the slow train standing. There was a grass bank to the north of the tracks at this point and, lying on the bank beside his cab, was the motorman enjoying the sun. He obviously didn't expect to be going anywhere soon. Then, a surprise. Having a rudimentary understanding of signalling I discovered the first electric train was stacked one gantry ahead of where we had stopped, clearly everyone was involved in this drama.

Without much enthusiasm we made our way into the next station where, having been switched to the slow line, we passed another steam-hauled train standing at the platform. Soon we built up a bit of speed, although not what I'd been hoping for, and returned to the up through. We stayed on the express tracks from there on but the excitement wasn't over yet.

I think it was at Fleet (?) that we eventually passed the cause of the delay; about an hour and a quarter had also now passed. An original Light Pacific stood rather forlornly on the slow line a few yards before the platform started, very sooty, paintless and surrounded by fire fighters, their appliance on the other side of the fence. I'd heard of the Bulleid's Achilles Heel and here was proof of their weakness. A sad sight for a worshipper!

You might think the excitement was over; but not quite. True we did have an uninterrupted journey the rest of the way to Waterloo yet not without further interest. After some miles we slowly started to overhaul another train and it was moving quite fast. One of the things I liked about the four-track line into Waterloo was the possibility of racing another train and feeling superior to something 'on the juice'. But this one was steam-hauled! We were doing about 60mph at this point and the other perhaps 55. And then the denouement. At the head of the other train with at least 10 up was the little Victorian looking 0-6-0 which had passed us when we had first come to a halt. It was working its heart out, obviously to the delight of its crew, and thrilling to witness. For the rest of the journey they gave us a good run for our money arriving at Waterloo not long after us. Victorian engineering was the real star.

This all really happened even if my memory of details are hazy, but one thing I cannot understand are the contradictions in my memory. Clearly it was before 1967 because that is when electrification west of Pirbright happened; but I also know all the old pre-Southern locos had been withdrawn long before this. Perhaps it didn't happen quite where I thought but at Woking and the location of the shamed pacific was Byfleet. In which case `64 or `65 is a more likely date. But it was now a long time ago.

Island Bottleneck

Jeffery Grayer

Scene of many a summer Saturday traffic jam, these are the notorious level crossing gates at Langston on the Hayling Island branch. This view looking towards Hayling Island reveals much detail with the crossing gates being of primary interest. The original LBSCR gates were replaced with these of typical SR pattern with cross bracing and split red warning discs. The Southern Railway warning notice remains in situ in this early 1960s view by the pedestrian wicket gates. The small timber shed on the right, outside which was located a six-lever ground frame, was provided for the use of the Crossing Keeper and that is no doubt his bicycle propped up against the side wall. This was also not the original ground frame but an ex-LSWR Mackenzie & Holland fitting. Due to the considerable road traffic on Summer Saturdays, plus the frequency of trains on this short branch line where 24 journeys each way were booked on Saturdays during the final Summer timetable in 1963, two men were required to operate the gates, signals and man the small Booking-Office-cum-Waiting-Room here which can be seen on the curving concrete platform; this in turn replaced an earlier wooden version in 1949/50. One of the crossing keepers, Mr O'Shea, was also a taxi driver and could often be seen on the platform wearing his taxi driver's cap hence it is almost certainly his black cab parked on the grass verge just beyond the crossing. The front of the green sign, the reverse of which is seen to the right of the taxicab, read 'Southern – Langston Station – Trains to Havant for Portsmouth, Brighton and London.' Until 1960 motorists were not only delayed by the railway crossing but also by the need to pay a toll to cross the only road bridge to the island. Closure of the line in November 1963, although a sad day for the travelling public and for enthusiasts, was no doubt welcomed by motorists who had previously been held up here. *Jeffery Grayer collection.*

More SR Inspections

Gerry Nichols

Wilton ('South' in BR days) looking east towards Salisbury. Ironically from once having two stations it now has none although the respective lines on which both were situated are still open.

J. Eyers/South Western Circle collection

NOTES OF INSPECTION. Wednesday and Thursday 20 and 21 August 1935.

Present:
Mr R. Holland Martin C.B. Chairman
Sir Herbert Walker K.C.B. General Manager
Mr. E. C. Cox. Traffic Manager
Mr. G. Ellson. Chief Engineer
Mr. W. H. Shortt. Divisional Engineer
Mr. P. Nunn. Divisional Superintendent.

1. WILTON. It was reported that the proposal for closer working between the Southern and Great Western railways is under enquiry, and a scheme is being prepared for the provision of a central signal box to replace the two now in use, in order to effect economy in working.

2. YEOVIL TOWN. It was noted that the new and improved covered way on the Main platforms had been completed, with the exception of that outside the new Parcels Office, for which tenders will be invited in the near future. With the completion of this, the conditions under which the large and valuable passenger train parcels traffic is dealt with will be greatly improved, and should give every satisfaction.

3. TEMPLECOMBE. In connection with an inspection of this station carried out by the Traffic Manager and the Chief Engineer, it has been found that the existing premises are in such an old and worn out condition that reconditioning them would be extremely expensive. The conclusion has therefore been reached that instead of doing this the station should be reconstructed.

A plan (No 10/2265/Y/16) has been prepared showing how this could be effected. The proposals embodied in this scheme were considered in detail, and generally approved, with the following amendments and additions:

(a) Signal Box. Although the under-structure of this is of solid masonry, the upper portion, which is timber, is in a worn out condition and should be renewed.

(b) Staff Offices. The scheme provides for the erection of two new rooms for the S.R. and S.& D. Permanent Way Inspectors. It is considered that the expense of this

Above: **Shuttle from Yeovil Junction at Yeovil Town station.**
J. Eyers/South Western Circle collection

Left: **An unusual image at Templecombe showing the course of the long disused connection between the down S. & D. line and the up West of England line – the latter may be seen on the embankment running left to right. The location also affords a glimpse of the hotch-potch of buildings that so typified so many railway locations in earlier times.**
J. Eyers/South Western Circle collection

can be minimised by the disused Goods Office being handed over to the Southern Railway Permanent Way Inspector and a room provided for the S.&D. Inspector in the Western end of the Tranship Shed. Only a small section of the Tranship Shed is now required for goods work, and there is, therefore, space enough to provide not only for the S.&D. Inspector, but also a room for the Chief Mechanical Engineer's Department store, and a Mess Room for the Chief Mechanical Engineer's men.

(c) Station Master's House. The scheme, if approved, will necessitate a new house being provided for the Station Master, and the Estate Agent is already considering where this can be placed.

(d) Access between the Main Station and the S.& D. Low Level Platform.

It would greatly facilitate the transfer of passengers between the S.& D. Line and the Main Station if there were a covered footpath leading from the low level platform to the upper station, giving access, preferably, to the down platform.

The view was expressed that if this were possible certain of the trains which now have to run to and from the high level, involving expensive engine working, need not do so and economy could be effected.

It was decided that representatives of the Southern Railway and the L.M.S. should be called upon to investigate this question, and submit a joint report thereon.

Subject to the foregoing an estimate to be prepared for the carrying out of this scheme, so that it may be submitted to the Directors for their approval before the end of the year.

4. AXMINSTER. It was pointed out that considerable difficulty is experienced in transferring luggage from the down platform to the Lyme Regis trains in the up side bay. Owing to the platforms being staggered, and the obstruction caused by the water column and signal box at the Western end of the platform, it is not possible to find a site for a sleeper crossing. It was stated that on busy days in the summer when there is a large transference of luggage, as many as 100 packages are dealt with by one train, and the risk in transferring these across the running lines by hand is considerable. It was, therefore, decided that a plan should be prepared showing how lifts could be provided with a gallery adjacent to the road over-bridge, and the Chief Engineer was requested to arrange for this.

5. SEATON JUNCTION. It was considered that the appearance of this station could be greatly improved if the surplus ground at the back of the down platform were planted with shrubs, and also if a line of shrubs were planted along the foot of the bank at the back of the Branch platform. The Divisional Engineer was instructed to arrange this.

6. SEATON. The difficulties experienced in handling the Summer Traffic at Seaton are considerable, owing to the extremely limited accommodation. These difficulties have been accentuated by the opening of a large Summer Camp. The weekend excursion traffic has also increased, and owing to the shortness of the platform, and the absence of run-round facilities, etc. the traffic cannot be handled as efficiently and expeditiously as it should be.

It has been recognised for some time past that general improvements are necessary at this station, and it has already been decided to include it in the list of New Works to be considered for approval during 1936. The Chief Engineer was, therefore, requested to prepare a plan embodying as its main features the following.

The platform to be lengthened to accommodate a train of 12 coaches.

A run-round road through the engine shed is to be provided for trains of this length.

In tipping for the necessary run-round road, space also to be allowed for putting in a long carriage siding outside the run-round road if conditions will allow. The present station building to constitute Parcels, Booking and Enquiry offices, and a new building including Booking Hall, Waiting Rooms, lavatory

Axminster: where luggage transfer issues, between down main line trains and branch services, were the cause for concern during the inspection.
J. Eyers/South Western Circle collection

The rebuilt Seaton Junction, concern here centred only on the appearance of the station with recommendations for the planting of shrubs.
J. Eyers/South Western Circle collection

Improvements were indeed made at the terminus at Seaton with two long platforms provided. These are the starting signals at the end of the platform.
J. Eyers/South Western Circle collection

accommodation, etc. to be designed in place of the present old structure. The platform to be raised to standard height and to be covered to a length of 300ft.

Seaton Holiday Camp. In connection with this new Summer Camp, it is understood 500 people are in residence at one time, a large proportion of these travelling to and from London on a Saturday, and there would appear to be a reasonable prospect of securing a train load in each direction on Saturdays during the Summer. If this could be done it would considerably relieve the pressure on other services, and avoid in many cases a change of train as well.

The Divisional Superintendent was instructed to put himself into communication with the Secretary of the Camp and consider with him how the railway services for the conveyance of passengers to and from the Camp can be improved generally.

7. SIDMOUTH. The Booking and Parcels Office at this station is quite inadequate for dealing with the summer traffic, and is also very dark.

A sketch was submitted showing how the office could be enlarged by taking in the passage way running from the Booking Hall to the Ladies' Room, access to the latter being given direct from the platform.

The Chief Engineer was asked to prepare a plan for this, and also to include the replacement of a portion of the platform roof outside the station offices in glass, and extend the covered way a further 150ft.

At the present time there is no footpath leading from the station entrance to the Junction of the two main roads, both of which are fairly busy. It was considered very desirable that such a footpath should be constructed, and the Divisional Engineer was instructed to negotiate with the local Borough Surveyor with a view to seeing what would be the best arrangement to suit the requirements both of the Local Authorities and the railway passengers, and report thereon.

Parking of Cars, Buses, etc. The space available for the parking of cars and buses on the forecourt is somewhat restricted. It could be enlarged by an alteration to the fence enclosing the Cattle Dock, thus giving a larger area for the parking of vehicles. The Divisional Engineer was instructed to carry out the work in consultation with the Divisional Superintendent.

Goods Shed. Although the Goods Shed is generally satisfactory for dealing with the Goods traffic, the work is hampered by there only being one bay for vans loading. As there is not sufficient floor space to allow for the construction of a second bay, it was decided that a plan should be prepared showing how an opening could be made in the end of the shed, so that vehicles backing up to this entrance could stand clear of the road leading to the coal sidings, and the Chief Engineer was requested to have a plan and estimate prepared for this work.

The exterior of Sidmouth station and as with many, looking more akin to a private house than railway property. The public entrance was around the left corner with goods yard access to the right.
J. Eyers/South Western Circle collection

Finally in this section, the junction of the Sidmouth branch and its connection with the main line at Sidmouth Junction – the station of the same name is out of sight to the left. In some respects it is surprising Sidmouth Junction was never rebuilt and enlarged considering the branch traffic that emanated from both Sidmouth and also Exmouth via Budleigh Salterton. Perhaps the Southern were content to leave the ensuing chaos to nearby Tipton St John!
J. Eyers/South Western Circle collection

8. SIDMOUTH JUNCTION. The Ladies Waiting Room is extremely dark, and can be greatly improved in this respect by a window being inserted in the wall separating this room from the General Room. The latter has excellent natural lighting, and the Divisional Engineer was given authority to carry out this improvement. At the same time it was decided that glass should be inserted in the platform roof outside the Booking Office, so as to improve the lighting of the latter, and this work is to be undertaken at the same time.

9. EXMOUTH BRANCH. In passing over the Exmouth Branch it was noticed that the service is a somewhat irregular one, and the General Manager instructed that a scheme should be prepared showing how a regular one-hourly service in each direction could be given throughout the day in the winter months, and a half-hourly service throughout the day in the summer months. It is understood that additional periods would have to be made during the one-hourly service period for the morning and evening business traffic.

The Traffic Manager was instructed to have a scheme prepared along these lines.

10. BRANCH LINE WORKING. It was noticed that, with the exception of the Seaton Branch, which is worked by Pull and Push trains, the local services in the Western area are all worked by two coach sets, involving the running round of the engine after each journey.

The Divisional Superintendent expressed the view that a more general use of Pull-and-Push sets would be a great advantage, and he was instructed to submit a report showing the number of sets that would be required to equip the whole of the services in this area in this way. At the same time the Traffic Manager was requested to consider whether the sets could be so arranged for trains to be made up of either two, four, six, or eight vehicles.

It was also noticed that the timing of some of the Branch Line trains is erratic, involving considerable delay at intermediate stations. The Divisional Superintendent was instructed to have the whole of the Branch Line services overhauled, and submit a report to the Traffic Manager.

11. TRAIN SERVICES. There would appear to be an absence of suitable connections between trains, both at Yeovil Town and Sidmouth Junction, and the Traffic Manager undertook to arrange for the Investigation Committee to overhaul the services, with a view to setting how the timetable could be improved in this respect.

12. ENGINE WORKINGS. When visiting Yeovil Town it was mentioned that this Depot has 14 engines, many of which are used for Passenger services. From an examination of the timetable it would appear that the local services between Salisbury and Exeter are broken up into too many sections, which include change of engine en-route. The Traffic Manager was requested to have the whole of the services overhauled, with a view to seeing if they can be revised in such a manner as to effect economy in engine power without detriment to the travelling facilities.

It becomes a question whether Yeovil Town is the most convenient place for stabling the engines, many of which have to run light for considerable distances.

The Investigation Committee to examine the workings, and see whether by redistribution, the number of engines employed could be reduced, or whether there are other places, such as Templecombe, where it would be more convenient to stable some of the engines with a view to avoiding light running.

13. HARDINGTON SIDINGS. It was mentioned that these sidings are not being used, and was decided that the question of closing them should be revived this year, in accordance with the decision arrived at in 1932.

A Prologue and the 'Wealdsman Rail Tour'
The Last Rites of Steam and Lines in Sussex Part 1
Les Price
Images by the Author

During the final days of steam there were numerous rail tours on the South-Western Division of the Southern Region to commemorate the dying days and subsequent line closures. There seemed to have been far fewer on the Central Section, even though these lines equally suffered at the hands of Dr Beeching. The first of those I experienced was 'The Wealdsman Rail Tour' organised by the Locomotive Club of Great Britain, on Sunday 13 June 1965.

As its title suggests it travelled through much of the 'Weald', an area of alternating sands and clays located between the North and South Downs stretching from Hampshire in the west across to Kent in the east. It covered much of 'The High Weald Area of Outstanding Natural Beauty'.

The intention of the tour was to visit a swathe of station closures plus two lines in Mid- and West Sussex for the very last time and also to mark the virtual extinction of steam in the Central Division. It was to be a very emotive trip. To quote the LCGB Itinerary for the journey; '...*with two line closures and the virtual elimination of steam traction in the Central Division of the Southern Region ..., the LCGB has arranged this important tour, embracing as much as possible of the County of Sussex. The 'Cuckoo' and Cranleigh lines both closed to passengers yesterday.*' What it failed to add was the closure to steam of Redhill and Eastbourne depots at the same time.

Rudgwick – and from the opposite end of our cover photograph for this issue. There is a definite kink in the running line at the end of the station as seen under the bridge, the left hand line serving as a headshunt from the goods yard.

Part of the expansive facilities at Christ's Hospital and which never fulfilled the promoters' and architect's ambitions.

The *yesterday* mentioned had been Saturday 12 June; during which I had spent the last day of passenger services on one of those two lines, the Cranleigh branch. Built as the Horsham & Guildford Direct Railway, its Act of inauguration was passed on 6 August 1860. But as with many railways of the period its progress was not without difficulties. The LBSCR finally took control of the formally independent company in 1862, but negotiations with landowners dragged on and it wasn't until 2 October 1865 that the route finally opened. It failed to reach its centenary by a mere four months.

After an early rise I left Waterloo on the first fast Portsmouth service of the day, the 7.50am departure, for which the second stop was Guildford at 8.26. This was in time to see the 7.55 from Horsham roll in at 8.42. The locomotive in charge was an Ivatt Class 2 2-6-2T No 41287 sporting a 75A (Brighton) shed plate; although by the previous May it had already become Guildford-based. It drew to a stand in the platform with safety valves blowing whilst the meagre few passengers disgorged. After reversal the train was prepared in readiness to form the 9.8am working 'down' to Baynards.

Together with others who wished to experience the last day of services, I hopped aboard and the train then dutifully called at Bramley and Wonersh before we came to Cranleigh, the principal station on the branch, a substantially-built crossing place. All was neat, tidy and well-kept; it certainly did not look like a station on the brink of closure. And it was quiet here: considering it was the last day of service the marked absence of passengers felt like a lull before the storm. Next was Baynards,

a most unlikely destination for a train. It didn't serve any nearby settlement and thus passengers must have been very few.

Nevertheless, it too was quite a substantial station. Built in brick, it comprised a Station Master's house, two waiting rooms, platform canopies, store sheds, a porch over the Booking Hall entrance and a Goods shed. What could have demanded such excess? The reason, of course, was the nearby Baynards Park, the residence of Lord Thurlow through whose estates the railway was built. He was a prominent Liberal politician of his day, a Paymaster- General in Gladstone's government. It was he who had required such facilities as a condition of the sale of his land.

At Baynards the numbers of final day mourners also appeared to be increasing. After running round the train No 41287 took the stock back to Guildford running bunker first as the 9.46 ex- Baynards. There was now time to spare before the same engine came back with the 10.34 from Guildford. I set out south-east towards Slinfold by a means I can no longer remember but arrived there in time to photograph that train approaching.

I hurried aboard and at 11.7 headed for Christ's Hospital, effectively the end of the branch line. Here it joined the Mid-Sussex from Horsham to Pulborough and Arundel Junction, with its other branch to Shoreham-by-Sea via Steyning. Eight minutes later I was stepping out on to a broad island platform, the western end of which was completely overgrown. This platform was canopied as was the opposite platform, since the 'Up' branch line was served by two platforms.

Never let it be said that the LBSCR scrimped when it came to building its stations. Christ's Hospital was built on the grand scale. It opened in 1902 primarily to serve the large Independent School of the same name which had moved out from London earlier that year. Five through tracks were served by seven platforms reflecting the large number of pupils expected daily.

Indeed the school partly funded the construction of the station, the main building of which was in the same style as the school itself. Two of the tracks had double facing platforms including the one on the Guildford Branch. But the anticipated traffic never materialised mainly because the school only ever accommodated boarders and a proposed nearby housing development also didn't materialise. The LBSCR had built a 'white elephant'.

Nikolaus Pevsner, the renowned architectural historian, variously described the station as, 'West Sussex's only memorable railway station...one of the best examples in southern England of an unaltered late Victorian railway building...a better building than the Hospital itself' and 'a perfect anthology of railway forms.'

But by 1965 it had become a desolate sight and I now had the time to explore the ghostly cobwebs. Despite pleas for preservation from historians the main station buildings were demolished in 1972. This destruction was described by contemporary historians as a 'mammoth act of vandalism' and 'a slaughter.'

At 12.13pm the 12.9 from Horsham ambled in behind another Ivatt 2-6-2T No 41299, running bunker first, having taken over from its sister engine on the previous turn; No 41299 was also now a Guildford (70C) allocated engine, which had accompanied No 41287 from Brighton in May 1964. The three route indicator discs displayed on the bunker read 'My Last Trip', one word on each disc. On its side tank someone had chalked the letters 'RIP'. After reposing amongst the weeds on the island platform for a scheduled but unexplained five minutes the train shuffled away at 12.18pm.

Following a service break at Horsham No 41287 returned 'up' the branch with the 3.9 to Guildford. I caught up with it at Cranleigh as she ran in at 3.39. Another of those unexplained interludes then followed as we sat in the platform for a scheduled ten minutes. The numbers of sightseers were beginning to swell. The train was well filled and passengers were hanging out of carriage windows. At that time the population of Cranleigh was about ten thousand and the proposal to close the line had surprisingly been met with little opposition. Nevertheless residents were now turning out to see the final trains.

At 3.49 the Guildford pulled out to a cacophony of detonators set off by the engine. After a visit to Rudgwick to witness further comings and goings it was time to pick up the 6pm from Horsham at Baynards at 6.21pm – the very last 'up' service train.

The final and most memorable sight was witnessed from the 6.20 ex-Portsmouth Harbour as it left Guildford at 7.18 for Waterloo; No 41287, with safety valves blowing and garlanded with ribbon, waiting patiently on one of the shed roads before heading the last scheduled 'down' passenger on the branch, the 7.34 from Guildford.

Sunday morning at Waterloo – conversation piece alongside No 34050 *Royal Observer Corps*. The engine is displaying its 10 year long-service badge on the cabside.

The following morning I didn't have to rise quite so early. 'The Wealdsman Rail Tour' was not due to depart from Waterloo until 9.54am. Standing at the head of the train was rebuilt 'Battle of Britain' Pacific No 34050 *Royal Observer Corps*, proudly displaying its 70D (Eastleigh) shed plate. She was well turned out, cleaned for the occasion and with no trace of escaping steam.

We left on time, making a cautious run out of the terminus through the reverse curves of the Vauxhall viaduct. According to the Itinerary, '...*there is no apparent reason for the twisting nature of the viaduct. The contractors had to avoid an old gasworks, long since gone, and the once fashionable and extensive Vauxhall Gardens, now modestly bordering South Lambeth Road, behind Coronation Buildings, an early-Edwardian LSWR estate.*'

Royal Observer Corps nudged her way out through Clapham Junction and the South Western suburbs of the Surrey stockbroker belt of Epsom, Leatherhead and Dorking, to Horsham. So sedately, in fact, that we arrived there seven minutes late. We had crossed the Surrey/West Sussex border, cruising at 65mph between Ockley and Capel and Warnham.

At Horsham the Pacific ran round the train in order to take it back the eight miles 'up' to Three Bridges. As might be expected running tender first, speed never rose above 46mph.

Here we were met by two locomotives to take us east, one of which I was to become familiar with on a subsequent rail tour. This was the Maunsell 'N' class 2-6-0 No 31411, based at Guildford. Piloting her was another Maunsell, 'U' Class 2-6-0 No 31803, also a Guildford loco. Only ten 'N's and seven 'U's were left in service by this time. After the change had been effected we left Three Bridges eight minutes down. Just south of the station, we forked east onto the former East Grinstead Railway.

This nominally independent line opened on Monday 9 July 1855 but really it had always been 'in tow' of the LBSCR. Foreseeing it as a future profitable extension to Tunbridge Wells, the LBSCR bought out the EGR in January 1865. Despite the financial privations of the LBSCR at the time, the completed route to Tunbridge Wells was eventually opened throughout on Monday 1 October 1866.

At Rowfant 'The Wealdsman' put in its first photographic stop, allowing passengers freedom to roam for fully seventeen minutes.

Three Bridges departure behind 31803 and 31411.

At this remote station the railway had cut a path through the estate surrounding Rowfant House owned at the time by Curtis M. Lampson, an American fur trader and vice-chairman of the Atlantic Telegraph Company. He agreed to sell his land cheaply to the LBSCR on the condition that a station would be provided together with the right to stop trains on request. The only other nearby residence, Worth Hall, was owned by John Nix, an LBSCR director. Did this just happen to be a coincidence?

Consequently Rowfant saw very little passenger traffic and even in Edwardian days shared, with Kingscote, the record for the least revenue taken for passenger journeys on the LBSCR. Despite the lengthy stop we still left two minutes behind schedule, sweeping through East Grinstead. Perhaps there was too much to distract the passenger here, with its overlapping station on two different levels! So on to the next call at Forest Row and another photographic stop. From West Sussex at East Grinstead we had now entered East Sussex and the western flank of the lovely Ashdown Forest. At last the summer sun began to shine.

The station here was opened on 1 August 1866 but in contrast to Rowfant it became one of the busiest on the line, enlarged in 1897 with the addition of a new platform on the 'down' side connected by a footbridge. A Goods Shed and two sidings completed the layout, now affording much greater opportunity for photography. Ironically, on closure of the line some eighteen months after our call, Forest Green was still taking over £5,000 per annum with over 200 commuters travelling daily to London from the station.

We left just a minute late at 12.31 for a gentle run through the sylvan setting of the forest and passed Hartfield, forever associated with the nearby 'Poohsticks Bridge'. Created by A.A. Milne in his book *Winnie the Pooh*, it was situated deep amongst the trees just to the south of the village and station.

At Ashurst Junction the train took the west to south fork of the triangle to Birchden Junction and ran through Eridge on

time at 12.49. Just a mile further on, at Redgate Mill Junction, the south-east fork was taken on to the 'Cuckoo Line,' which ran due south through pastoral country. We were now in the heart of the High Weald. Here the former double track from Ashurst reduced to a single line, falling at 1 in 88 towards Rotherfield. There were two short tunnels, the longest of which was about 200 yards, just north of Heathfield.

The line's name derived from a tradition observed at an annual fair held each April at Heathfield, whereby a lady released a cuckoo from a basket; supposedly being 'the first cuckoo of spring'. In consequence the route became jocularly nicknamed the 'Cuckoo Line' by drivers locally. We had now passed Rotherfield and Mayfield, the suffix 'field' emphasising the rustic nature of the line.

On 1 September 1897, which happened to be the seventeenth anniversary of the Heathfield to Groombridge extension, the 8.18am from Eastbourne was involved in a derailment on a sharp curve at Clayton's Farm just south of Mayfield leaving the track on a sharp curve and rolling down the embankment. The driver of the locomotive involved, an LBSCR Stroudley D1 Class 0-4-2T No 297 *Bonchurch*, was killed and several passengers in the wooden coaches injured. The conclusion drawn was that the track was not substantial enough for high-speed running.

Certainly we were not following suit and shortly after came to a stand at Heathfield. The old name for the town is 'Heffle', thus its annual fair is actually called the 'Heffle Cuckoo Fair'. This time the origin goes back to 1316 when the Bishop of Chichester was granted a charter to hold a weekly market and annual fair here.

It was one of those small British towns whose colloquial name was only known to the local inhabitants. As well as the fair there is a carnival parade and it is 'Dame Heffle' who releases the cuckoo from her basket. It is still thriving to this day but because of the rarity of obtaining a cuckoo you are more likely to see a pigeon!

Photo stop at Heathfield. The engine whistle had just sounded calling the passengers back to the train.

This small market town has a population of over eleven thousand and was the main station on the line between Eridge and Hailsham. Consequently it had generous station buildings and a spacious goods yard; another example of the LBSCR's largesse. In 1896 the Company drilled for water at the north end of the station but at a depth of 312 feet found natural gas instead.

Subsequently the railway began to use this gas to light the station and continued to do so until February 1934 when it converted to use town gas. If my memory serves me right I think it was at this station I saw passengers coming out of an unlocked platform office door (presumably the Parcels Office) with handfuls of paper luggage labels; some of them marked LBSCR.

The next call was at Hellingly for a further photographic stop before joining the South-Coast main line at Polegate where we stopped for seven minutes whilst the locomotives were watered, before passing Stonecross Junction at 2.29, two minutes down. We were then treated to a non-stop run along the Coast to Hastings arriving at 2.47, five minutes before time. With a top speed of 58mph between Bexhill and St. Leonards, the schedule was obviously not too demanding.

Now the pair of 2-6-0s ran round the train. Running tender-first we passed Bopeep Junction at 3.9pm, one minute early, before attaining their highest speed, on the return, of 56mph between Cooden Beach and Norman's Bay Halt. Arrival at Eastbourne at 3.35pm was two minutes ahead of schedule.

Prior to the closure of Brighton Depot to steam on 13 June 1964 and the introduction of diesel units to the 'Cuckoo Line', the mainstay of power became BR Standard Class 2-6-4 Tanks. Fittingly with their proud local connection, the Class having been built at Brighton Works, No 80144 was supplied to provide steam power for trains on the last day of services on Saturday 12 June. It had been out-shopped from Brighton in September 1956. After initial deployment to the Great Central at Neasden (34E), it returned to Brighton at the end of 1959, spending the next phase of its life in Sussex.

This would also account for how it came to be at Eastbourne the following day to be attached to the rear of 'The Wealdsman', in order to release the pair of Moguls from the buffers at Eastbourne. From December 1963 to June 1965 No 80144 was a Redhill (75B)-allocated engine. Later, officially from 8 June, it had been re-allocated into store at Salisbury (70E).

June 1965 had seen steam officially banned from the Central Division, resulting in the closure of not only Redhill MPD but those at Tunbridge Wells West and Eastbourne as well. It is therefore highly likely that No 80144 was the very last engine to be serviced at Eastbourne. The steam shed officially closed on 13 June 1965. *(*thebrightonbranchofaslef.yolasite.com)* It would also be the last steam shed to close on the Central Division.

Did this engine then go direct from here to Salisbury afterwards? Certainly storage at Salisbury was brief as it went to Eastleigh six months later and from there to Nine Elms (70A) in late January 1966. Three months later it was condemned and sent to Bird's at Bridgend for cutting up. The lifespan of the engine had been less than ten years, half of which was spent in Sussex, based at Brighton and then Redhill.

A break of just over an hour was given at Eastbourne to allow the two Moguls to be serviced. We left at 4.40pm and after passing Willingdon Junction once again, had completed all three sides of the triangle. There then ensued a sprightly run through Polegate and Lewes up to Haywards Heath, where we arrived, just a couple of minutes late. This was despite a top speed of 62mph between Berwick and Glynde and 56mph through Plumpton.

Arriving at Haywards Heath the pair had completed their task and, after detaching, went off to Redhill. Meanwhile, after servicing, the 'Battle of Britain' had made its way down from Three Bridges to retake charge of the train. This time *Royal Observer Corps* fairly scampered down the Brighton main line, topping 60mph beyond Hassocks, and at Preston Park took the western Brighton avoiding line to Hove for the onward Coast line to Shoreham-by-Sea.

At Shoreham Junction we diverged onto the Adur Valley line to Horsham; also known as the Steyning Line. Its construction emerged following the territorial wars between the LBSCR and the LSWR. Both companies promoted lines through Steyning during the Railway Mania years of the mid-nineteenth century but the following financial downturn put an end to both proposals. In the aftermath and with the intervention of local people, the LBSCR proposal was resurrected and won the day. The line we were now traversing opened on 16 October 1861.

The second station up this branch was the principal one, Steyning, where we arrived two minutes early, for another photographic stop of fifteen minutes. In the early evening sunshine the tour participants, together with some locals, were thronging around the engine taking their pictures. How often would a 'Battle of Britain' have called at this station?

Steyning is a small market town in West Sussex at the north end of the Adur Gap in the South Downs, with a population, at the time, of about five and a half thousand. Steam had continued to prevail on the Brighton to Horsham services via Steyning until May 1964 when Brighton Depot (75A) was about to close to steam. Diesel units were then introduced to provide the branch service and hopefully save it. But, despite great protestations and as important as it was to local people the Steyning line eventually lost its battle for survival and closed on 7 March 1966.

Again the LBSCR had provided a fairly substantial main station building here. For many years in the previous century, as well as passengers, the station's main traffic was animals, notably horses for the important Wednesday market in the adjacent 'Market Field'. Of course, by 1965, all this had gone. But there was still an unusually large three storey warehouse maintained in good condition in the goods yard and it would be interesting to know of its original purpose.

The stewards on the train did their work well at Steyning and we left promptly at 6.30pm for the sixteen miles journey onward to Horsham. We had now gone full circle around Sussex. The train reversed yet again and we were joined on the rear by a pair of two Q1 Class 0-6-0s Nos 33006 and 33027, both then Nine Elms (70A) engines, having recently been transferred from Guildford.

Eventide at Baynards and the final photo stop, Nos. 33027 and 33006 are in charge.

So we headed south out of Horsham crossing on to the Cranleigh line at Christ's Hospital for the very last trip up to Guildford. The evening sun was still burning brightly as we arrived at Baynards for the final photographic stop, on time at 7.24. Again a posse of passengers took to the tracks and throughout the former goods yard to record their final memories of the line.

At 7.39 the train solemnly set out for the run to Waterloo where its journey had commenced eleven hours earlier. For some reason best known to the organisers (possibly engineering works) we did not take the recognised route up the South Western main line but instead went via Effingham Junction and Hampton Court Junction, stopping at London Road (Guildford) to set down. The latter may also provide an alternative clue for the diversion.

This was quite a special and emotive rail tour, covering the majority of secondary routes through Sussex. Two of them had been axed, another followed nine months later and the next in eighteen months' time. From becoming a county well served with lines, by 1 January 1967 when the Three Bridges to Tunbridge Wells service succumbed, Mid-Sussex had become a virtual railway desert. The last short stub from Hailsham, on the Cuckoo Line, to Polegate lingered on until 8 September 1968 when that piece also finally succumbed.

From the evidence of this tour alone, it can be seen that one of the major victims of the Beeching cuts were small market towns throughout the country, many of which were in Sussex. It is little wonder then, that in some cases, this is now being reviewed. But for the many with subsequent land development, it is far too late.

So this would be the last comprehensive tour of Mid-Sussex lines. As noted, after May 1964, the last remaining steam depots, at Redhill and Eastbourne, closed in June 1965, thereby virtually eliminating steam from the Central Division. The sole remaining secondary route, Eridge to Uckfield and Lewes, in East Sussex and an important diversionary route from London to Brighton, will be discussed in Part 2.

The Waterloo & City Railway Electric (and Steam) Locomotives

John Perkin

Electric loco SR 74, the one most will recall. Its duties were primarily moving coal wagons for the associated power stations at Durnsford Road but we suspect could also be involved in shunting stock. In the background is the elevated siding leading to the power station. The locomotive's original purpose had been to rescue trains that might have failed in the tunnels although the reliability of the electric trains from the outset meant it was rarely, if ever, needed, hence the move to Durnsford Road.
R. C. Riley/The Transport Treasury

As a retired Chartered Electrical Engineer all forms of electric traction are of interest, the more obscure the better. These two locomotives were seldom seen except by commuters in the case of 74S, and more recently the preserved 75S.

The Waterloo and City Railway – W&CR

Built as an independent tube railway 1 mile 46 chains in length from Waterloo below the Thames to the City of London and opened on 11 July 1898, the line ran in two tunnels twelve feet in diameter with sharp curves and steep gradients with power from a central rail at 500V dc supplied by the Power Station in Lower Marsh, Waterloo.

An Armstrong lift was installed to the north of Waterloo station and was long enough to accommodate one coach or two coal wagons for the power station. The wagons were shunted through the station to be emptied into the 200 ton capacity power station bunkers via another hoist.

The W&CR was absorbed by the LSWR on 1 January 1907. In 1915 the power supply was transferred to the LSWR power station at Wimbledon and the voltage increased to 600V. For some time afterwards the former power plant at Lower Marsh was retained as a stand-by.

In 1940 the Southern Railway provided new rolling stock for the line and converted the track to its standard side third rail contact system. Following the formation of British Railways, later Network SouthEast, in 1993 the line was again transferred, this time to London Underground and following upgrading and conversion once again, this time to the four-rail system, the 1940 SR stock was replaced by London Underground stock.

W&CR not numbered/LSWR 'The Green Engine'/SR 74/BR(SR) S74 & 74S

DS74 (known as the 'Green Engine') was to a design attributed to Dugald Drummond, and built at Eastleigh Works [W&CR Oakwood Press] (although some think it may have been built at Nine Elms …). Electrical equipment was provided by the firm of Dick, Kerr for the LSWR in 1899. The engine was of the Bo-Bo Electric (camel type) and designed to haul full-length trains which might become stuck or break down in the tunnel. Such though was the reliability of the first trains it was very seldom needed. It was fitted with four 60hp Siemens gearless motors and took power from a central third rail at 500 volts dc with the return through the running rails. Cab width was restricted by 9' 8" due to the size of the tube tunnel. Westinghouse air brakes were fitted powered by compressed air stored in two cylinders carried on the side opposite the single cab side cab door. These tanks needed to be recharged every four hours. It shared some work at Waterloo with the 4-wheeled loco shunting coal/ ash wagons. In 1915 it was transferred to the newly-built Durnsford Road Power Station, Wimbledon, and used for shunting coal wagons up and down the 1 in 45 slope to the bunkers. For this task it was modified with new geared tramway type E1 motors of about 85hp. It also now had side shoes and was converted to 600 volts dc and also painted green, possibly malachite with red buffer beams. A single tramway type controller and air brake valves were fitted.

In SR days it was allocated the number 74 in the Plant and Machinery series but the number was not carried.

Durnsford Road Power Station closed in May 1958 and the loco was stored. The engine was withdrawn in July 1965, sold for scrap, leaving Wimbledon on a well wagon.

Waterloo & City Railway – W&CR No 2/LSWR 'The Brown Engine' /SR 75/BR(SR) S75 & 75S

Built by Siemens of Stafford at a cost of £1,653. The builder's number was '6' – one of the first electric locos in the UK (the works plate only bore the build date of 1898).

Electric loco SR 75 which spent nearly all its working life underground but has since emerged into the daylight to be preserved as part of the National Collection.

This was a smaller 'Bo' Electric machine. Clause 155 of the build contract for 1897 between the W&C and Siemen Bros and Co, who supplied the generating and other electrical equipment for the line, makes for interesting reading; '*There must also be provided an electrical shunting and coal- hauling locomotive of 4' 8 ½" gauge, complete with motor or motors and a starting, stopping and regulating appliance similar to those in the cabs of the motor cars. It must have enough power to haul or push four fully-loaded coal trucks up an incline of 1 in 60 at not less than 8mph, and must have Westinghouse compressed air and hand brakes, with buffers and couplings that can be used either with ordinary railway wagons or with the W&C coaches.*'

It was allocated to Waterloo (Waterloo and City) for shunting coal wagons between the Waterloo Armstrong lift and the Abbott lift for raising them to the level of the original power station that

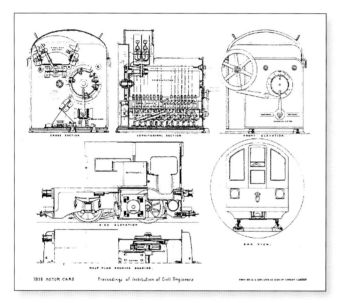

supplied electricity to the W&C, empty wagons also being returned with ash from the power stations. A further task was in shunting W&C stock and also on engineering trains. Another description of the wheel arrangement was 'Ao+A'. The engine was fitted with two Siemens 60hp motors, nose-suspended with single reduction gears, the same type as fitted to the passenger cars on the line. Initially wound for 500v dc these were later altered to 600v dc. Of necessity, the cab floor was installed below the level of the frames due to the restricted loading gauge. There was a driving position at one end only but large windows at the other end permitted running in both directions.

The engine controller was similar to that used on the original 1898 electric stock operated by a large wheel on a horizontal shaft. The locomotive was fitted with air brakes and was indeed fitted with the dual drawgear specified in the contract. It was stated to have been given the Number 2 by the W&C.

As with its sister engine, it was taken over by the LSWR in 1907, presumably painted brown but without a number. It is believed that it was numbered 75 by the SR. Following modernisation and conversion to third rail, in 1940 it was withdrawn and stored at Peckham Rye depot.

In the early 1950s, it was painted light green at the Waterloo W&C depot with red buffer beams and black framing. Lion and wheel emblems were fitted, folklore has it these were scrounged from Stewarts Lane!

It was painted mid green again in 1962, the paint carefully applied around the emblems, with a silver roof and 'S75' stencilled in 1" high white characters on the frame near the buffer beam. It was used until March 1968 when, following a serious electrical fire, it was stored until officially withdrawn in October 1968. Around this time it was then lifted up the hoist, and subject to further store at Wimbledon and later the former Pullman works at Preston Park, Brighton, having been earmarked for the National Collection. The engine moved to York in December 1977.

The end for No 74S. After some years in store it was eventually sold for scrap and is seen here being shunted on a well wagon (by No 34023) prior to departing from Wimbledon for the very last time for scrap.

In 1979 it was restored externally to SR livery, a bright orange-brown colour lined in orange with black edging and lettered SR and 75.S in two lines. The front boxes were black in post-1943 condition with side 3rd rail pick up shoes. It was certainly well travelled for it moved again to Swindon in 1990 with the NRM on-tour exhibition, returning to York NRM in 1993.

Manning Wardle No 407, originally Pioneer, built by MW in 1876.

Between mid-1897 and June 1899 this diminutive 0-4-0ST was used as the temporary shunter on the W&C line. Initially purchased from the contractor R. T. Relf in August 1881, the engine had previously seen service on the Sutton Harbour and Chasewater branches in Plymouth. This and a sister engine were then stored at Exmouth for a period after 1891 before eventually being sent to Nine Elms works. *Pioneer* emerged nameless as No 407 and was sent to Guildford to act as shed pilot. It was from here that it was then sent to the W&C, moving again in mid-1899 to Poole to work on the quays. A further move took place when, from April 1904 it spent four months assisting with engineering work on the quadrupling of the main line between Pirbright Junction and Basingstoke. Further engineering assistance was then given on the extension of the branch from Amesbury to Bulford. Duplicated as No 0407 it returned to light duties piloting or shunting at Brunswick Wharf or on hire to the Portsea Island Gas & Light Co, and also Bournemouth Corporation. Laid aside and offered for sale in December 1913, no purchaser came forward and consequently it was repaired in October 1915 and returned to Guildford once more as shed pilot. It was finally laid aside with a firebox 'practically worn out' in February 1919; this time there was no reprieve and having rusticated for over two years the engine was broken up in September 1921.

No 407 seen at Nine Elms where it languished for a time in between 'secondments elsewhere'.

Literally the end for No 407 at Eastleigh c1921, aged 45. Its condition does not need words and there would be no reprieve.

Acknowledgements

With many thanks to Graham Hallett, John Harvey & John Russell for their assistance.

References

Historic Electric Loco Nears Retirement. P. F. Winding. *Model Railways Constructor*, March 1959.

DC Electric Trains & Locomotives in the British Isles. R.L. Vickers. David & Charles 1986.

The Waterloo & City Railway. John C. Gillham. Oakwood Press 2001.

Diesel & Electric Locomotive Recognition Guide. Colin J. Marsden. Ian Allan 2011.

Non-steam Locomotives on British Railways, Part Three. *HMRS Journal Volume 20*, No 12.

The Miscellaneous Locos of the Southern – Part 7. Barry Fletcher.

LSWR Locomotives, The Adams Classes. D. L. Bradley. Wild Swan Publications. 1985.

Rebuilt
The Letters and Comments Pages

As mentioned upon in the Introduction, to this issue, the past few months have brought a bumper crop of items received for inclusion. Thank you all and apologies if it turns out your letter or e-mail is not included. Be assured we do read them all.

In no particular order we start with **Stuart Hicks** and 'Knowle' in SW50. Stuart correctly points out that a stray sentence worked its way in as the second sentence in the first paragraph at the foot of p 36. Please therefore ignore reference to that starting 'By 1908...'. We also have an EPB not a SUB in the snow scene on p38. Stuart adds, 'The set number gives it away (and the roller blind head code, most SUBs used stencils to the end) but I think that SUBs were unusual (if not unknown) on the eastern section by then.' He concludes with a suggestion as to our mystery image on p 7. More on that anon!

Next from **Eric Youldon** who makes a most interesting personal observation concerning the S.C. Townroe image of the painted front end to No 30852, see p 16 of SW50. He recalls, 'That very day I was travelling between Bournemouth and Eastleigh and passed the special on its way down in the pouring rain and briefly spotted the rather grotesque front decorating.' A further note from Eric states, 'John Click's articles are interesting once you get used to his notebook style of presentation. He mentions that 21C4 (SW49) was the last MN turned out new in SR green – which is not correct. All those numbered up to and including 21C6 came out in green and 21C7 was similarly in green but promptly repainted black, possibly before leaving the works. Hence the only engines that were black from new were 21C8, 21C9 and 21C10 in 1941.' Eric adds an interesting snippet to the headcode seen on Drummond's 'bug' – p 80. 'This was not actually a route code but simply an indication that 'His Nibs' was out and about!' Finally on p 92 and the picture of the worded warning notice, Eric adds that the board was repeated at the end of the down platform whilst the wording was also shown on the reverse side.

We receive an amount of most useful correspondence from Eric Youldon and so here is one especially for him. A Drummond 4-6-0 somewhere on the four-track section east of Basingstoke and portrayed as working well. Obviously a painting or recolour postcard, its origins are unknown.

Now from **Trevor Hodgson**. 'Many congratulations on producing Southern Way 50, nice touch with the gold lettering.

I am a few issues behind at the moment but cannot resist a quick flick though it, no doubt you have received a few mails pointing out that the photograph on p 50 is not of Midford as stated but a good interior view of Binegar.

Midford box only had 16 levers, of the Stevens pattern, and was a double to single line, where the picture shows double line block instruments on the shelf, interestingly Southern on the down line and Midland on the up.'

Colin Mason is one of several readers who have helped with the identification of the mystery photo on p 7 of issue 50, which is Station Road, Strood, looking south-east. 'The L1 is heading a down train on the LCDR route, shortly to cross the Medway into Rochester. The electric units are 2-HAL types, identified by the smooth front and round-edged windows, introduced for the 1939 electrification scheme to Gillingham and Maidstone, and parked in sidings across the running lines heading to Maidstone on the SER route. Strood station is some distance behind the photographer beyond the junction with the loop connecting Rochester bridge to Strood station (LCDR to SER). The unusual bridge which the L1 is about to cross avoids increasing the gradient climbing out of the valley up to Sole Street whilst maintaining adequate clearance underneath for trains.

Incidentally the lower photo of Clapham yard includes the house where I was born, 4th chimney stack from the left in Oberstein Road, above the centre of the carriage shed gable, where I spent my early years watching trolleybuses pass the end of Brussels Road until a family move to a house overlooking New Wandsworth goods yard.'

Mike King adds information on another location, this time p 1 of SW50. 'One comment (which no doubt others will have already pointed out to you) – the "Folkestone" picture is Dover Priory and the train is coming up from Marine – but whether they are water tanks or oil tanks from one of the harbour fuelling points I am not sure. No headcode displayed, so might it be a shunt move?'

Mike also speaks of the 'mystery' view. 'Station Road, Strood, where the LCDR line from Victoria (where the L1 and Maunsell restriction 1 set have come from) crosses over the line from Maidstone West, where the 2-HAL units have come from. The road is now the B2012 and the surroundings look rather different, but the bridges are still recognisable.

And finally, the special on p 79 looks to be the LCGB 'Southern Counties Ltd' of 24 February 1957, which started at Marylebone and visited the Oxted line, the Bluebell Railway (before preservation) and Brighton, then along the coast to Havant, a trip over the Hayling branch, on to Portsmouth and then back to Waterloo. Needless to say, a lot of locos were involved, including a Brighton Atlantic for the outward run (from Kew Bridge onwards) and a 'Schools' from Portsmouth back to Waterloo. 'Terriers' were of course used over Langston Bridge but whether the stock went to the Island or passengers decamped to the strengthened branch train I do not know.' (See also http://www.sixbellsjunction.co.uk/50s/570224lc.html)

Now from **Chris Heaps** a chain of correspondence which started with a comment over Richard Simmons' recent article (SW50) which referred to the April 1987 closure of the up line between East Putney and Point Pleasant Junction. 'The article by Richard Simmons refers to the closure of the up line between East Putney and Point Pleasant Junction with effect from April 1987, and to the fact that it had rarely been used by passenger trains since the withdrawal of the Waterloo-Wimbledon via East Putney electric service in May 1941.

An unusual train that used the upline over the flyover across the four Windsor lines in its last years was the VSOE Pullman returning to Victoria from Brockenhurst hauled by Class 33 No 33 056 *The Burma Star*. As President in 1983/84 of the Holborn Law Society, I had chartered the train on Saturday, 19 May 1984, for society members and friends for a journey from London to Brockenhurst (for Beaulieu) which travelled out via Dorking (pick-up) and the Mid-Sussex line but returned on the South Western Main Line and turned left at Wimbledon to reach Victoria via East Putney. It was probably the first time that the VSOE had traversed the Mid-Sussex line and certainly surprised not only District Line passengers on station platforms but also some passengers on the train who had not expected to be travelling on the London Underground system.

Just before the date of the trip, I was asked by the VSOE office if there would be space to enable six journalists and their partners from the USA to join us. We were happy to agree, and I believe that their enjoyment of the VSOE experience was greatly enhanced by meeting so many cheerful legal luminaries, many of whom had dressed up for the occasion and were attired in morning dress or boating blazers and the like. One of the guests could easily have been mistaken for the late Queen Mary.

I hope that this tit-bit may be of interest to your readers in your Rebuilt section. I have also run to earth the Special Traffic Arrangements documents (for both Central and South Western Division). These show that our special (1Z20) was of eight Pullman cars and two Baggage vans, and give the following times:

10.32 dep. Victoria
11.15 arr. Dorking (pick-up)
13.22 arr. Brockenhurst
16.35 dep. Brockenhurst
18.07 pass Wimbledon
18.15 pass East Putney
18.17 pass Point Pleasant Junction.'

Chris kindly continues on the topic of Jessie's Seat featured in SW46.

'In his article in SW 46 – *Two Accidents on Gomshall Bank* – John Burgess explained how the unusual topiary on the line-side commemorated a fatal accident between Gomshall and Chilworth on the Redhill – Reading branch of the South Eastern Railway on Leap Day, 29 February 1892.

Leap days at weekends are rare, but this year (2020) 29 February fell on a Saturday. To mark the occasion, the North Downs Line Community Rail Partnership Steering Group (of which I am Vice-Chairman) and Great Western Railway organised a special train from Reading to Redhill and back, which paused

North Downs Community Rail Partnership Steering Group special train at Reading on 29 February 2020 prior to departure. (See accompanying letter from Chris Heaps.) Left to right: Sir Peter Hendy, David Daniels/Brunel (Community Rail Development Manager) and Matthew Golton. *Chris Heaps*

adjacent to Jessie's Seat in both directions. A minute's silence was observed on the outward journey, and a posy of primroses was placed on the seat by the driver on the return journey.

Amongst the passengers on board were Sir Peter Hendy (Chairman of Network Rail); Matthew Golton (Acting MD of GWR); John Ellis (the last General Manager of the Southern Region of BR); and representatives of the CRP and local communities. Class 165 No 165 124 was adorned with a headboard at Reading, but unfortunately the absence of a lamp bracket on a Class 165 and modern Health and Safety requirements meant that it had to be removed before the train left. It is hoped that the headboard will in due course be erected either next to the topiary or at Chilworth station.

I attach a photograph of the special before departure from Reading, featuring (left to right) Sir Peter Hendy, David Daniels/Brunel (Community Rail Development Manager) and Matthew Golton.

Patient enthusiasts at Epsom on that day would also have seen – at 10.03 – a Diesel and Electric Group Chartex from London Bridge to London Bridge via Portsmouth Harbour formed of a Class 73 + 4TC; and – at 17.10 – an LT/BR Waterloo to Victoria via Portsmouth Railtour hauled by LT locomotive *Sarah Siddons*.'

Continuing on the topic of the East Putney line in SW50. **Nick Stanbury** writes, 'Richard Simmons' article on the SR route through East Putney (SW50) merits some amplification in terms of passenger traffic post-1941. As he described, the line between Wimbledon and Point Pleasant Junction remained in regular use for empty stock, excursion and milk trains,

especially those needing to run to or from the Windsor Lines at Clapham Junction and, if necessary, the West London Line. One such use was by some of the electric 'race specials' between Waterloo and Kempton Park or Hampton Court (for Hurst Park). The steep gradient up from Point Pleasant often required 'down' milk and other heavier trains to be piloted (typically by an M7) to East Putney or beyond.

In addition to the varying handful of scheduled passenger trains that he mentions, its use as a diversionary route had some unusual aspects. I recall a winter weekend in the late 1960s (the precise date eludes me) when engineering work between Wimbledon and Earlsfield totally precluded use of at least the up Slow line. At Wimbledon station, the track was severed about half-way along the up Slow platform and slewed left to connect with the similarly-treated adjacent bay road, necessitating some noticeable packing and (unless the PW people were very lucky) some specially-cut rails. Under the control of a hand-signalman, up trains were brought to a stand just before the slewing and, after completing station business, continued to Waterloo via East Putney, not stopping before Clapham Junction. Passengers for Earlsfield were required to travel via Clapham Junction, changing there to the next down stopping service, the down lines and services being totally unaffected, at least on that occasion. (I need hardly add that I made the unusual round trip by the economical purchase of a Wimbledon – Earlsfield day return.)

It is not always appreciated that the LSWR built the line beyond East Putney as far as the Middlesex side of its Putney Bridge, where it made an end-on junction with the District Railway, although nothing but District trains have ever ventured beyond East Putney in passenger service. Responsibility for the maintenance of the line (including the bridge) remained that of the LSWR and its successors until at least the eventual transfer to LUL in 1994. When an engineers' possession precluded the District service from running south of Putney Bridge, a replacement shuttle electric service could be provided between the LSWR 'up ' platform and Wimbledon, using SR stock (headcode P or 86). *London Railway Record* (issues 39/40) includes 1950s photographs of such an engineers' train (700 class No 30692 in charge) standing in the down District platform at East Putney with an EPB set on the shuttle in the adjacent LSWR platform. LRR magazines also include further photos and correspondence relating to East Putney events.'

Now from **Jeremy Clarke**. 'Sorry to bother you but someone has made a nonsense of a couple of sentences on p 73 SW50. I wrote "....within the Borough at Selhurst, Thornton Heath and Norbury. The other two travel via Crystal Palace, which is also served by two 'fasts' going to London Bridge." For some reason the piece has appeared as "...... Norbury en route via Tulse Hill and Peckham Rye. The other two call at Norwood Junction which is also served......" In other words a piece in sentence 2 has been deleted and another – which frankly really is nonsensical – has been added quite unnecessarily in sentence 1. Will you please note it as and when?' *Of course – Ed.*

Alan Holmewood adds some comments on SW50, a couple may already have been repeated but all are nevertheless included below. 'Title Page: I'm pretty sure that the location of the photograph is Dover Priory rather than Folkestone. P 38: Unit 5772 was a 2-EPB, not a 4-SUB. 'Croydon Tangle' p 72: The lamp attached to the distant signal was the Coligny-Welch lamp, not as shown. P 85: The Isle of Wight Constabulary may have included a PC McCloud in its ranks, but I suggest that the railwayman was A.B. MacLeod!! Lines & Services Dr Beeching did not close: *Passenger Services over Unusual Lines* records the booked service for 2020 over the Point Pleasant Junction to East Putney spur as:

Monday – Friday 00.42 Waterloo to Strawberry Hill, 01.05 and 23.12 Waterloo to Basingstoke/Southampton, 04.54 and 22.54 Basingstoke to Waterloo

Saturday the 23.12, 04.54 and 22.54 services

Sunday the 00.42 and 01.05 services

Passenger Services over Unusual Lines can be accessed via the Branch Line Society's website with copies back to 1963 freely accessible.'

Next from **John Davenport** on SW50. 'P 87 East Putney. Down milk empties from Clapham Junction to Exeter (or Yeovil) had been 3.54pm via East Putney before my spotting days in the 1940s. This was a weekday train with a different time on Saturdays. Were there recent comments somewhere about the provision of a banker as well to East Putney after one or two problems?'

Alan Postlethwaite adds to the comments on the 'mystery image'. 'May I be the first to suggest why the 6-LAV was at

Strood. (*Well, one of them, Alan – Ed.*) It may have been to transfer a ship's company from Portsmouth to Chatham, running via Brighton, East Croydon and the Birkbeck loop onto the LCDR main line to Chatham, then stabled overnight at Strood. Heave-ho, me hearties!' (But again others have suggested the sets were HAL types...)

Peter Clark has some notes on SW49. 'The EMU S5210 shown on p 57 is an early 4-EPB although it looks at first sight like a 4-SUB.

With regard to Derby-Sulzer Type 2 diesel locomotives on loan to the Southern Region in 1959, to the best of my recollection these were D5000-14 and D5017, a total of sixteen although odd ones returned to the LMR during the period.

Arthur Tayler's (not Taylor) photograph of D5002 has been published elsewhere and shows it arriving at Minster on an Ashford-Ramsgate via Canterbury West train in January 1961 (although the date was once given as 1960 but I don't think the conductor rail was in place by then).

The coal train is not at Martin Mill as the platforms here were linked by a subway, not a footbridge.

I think the location is Selling in which case the train is conveying empty wagons to Snowdown Colliery or Shepherdswell (for Tilmanstone).

The scene at Selling is much changed nowadays but the down siding, though long since disconnected, is still there under a line of trees.'

Now for something a little different from **Gerry Nichols**.

'Going through the Sid Nash photo collection, I came across this photograph which was not taken by Sid but has no information as to the photographer.

I believe that the image was taken from Purley Station on 14 August 1954 when ex-GWR engine No *5956 Horsley Hall* was allowed to go from Kensington Olympia to Redhill with the 7.35am Birkenhead to Margate and Ramsgate through train. Normally this train ran via Reading and Redhill but on this day an overbridge collapsed between Guildford and Shalford Junction. There was time to divert this train via the West London

Relics of yesteryear are still to be found – this at Staines. Colin Martin

line as were the 10.40 Birmingham to Hastings, the 10.40 Birmingham to Margate and the 9.57 Wolverhampton to Margate. Richard Hardy at Stewarts Lane was hard pressed to find motive power and crews to take over from the Western Region engines, managing two moguls. The Stewarts Lane crew were happy to continue with the Hall and it was thought that as the 43xx moguls were allowed, that the Hall was similarly permitted. Only on arrival at Redhill was the fact that Halls were not cleared for the Brighton line evident and the engine was summarily removed and sent to Redhill shed. It was eventually 'repatriated' overnight on 20 August travelling via Earlswood to Clapham Junction where it transferred to the Western Section Windsor Lines to access the West London Extension. This was subject to a speed limit of 25mph and 10mph through station platforms, the issue being the outside cylinder clearance.'

Next from **Nicholas Owen**, 'What a marvellous pleasure it was to savour the latest Southern Way – so nice to be able to delve into a string of fascinating railway stories, and forget for a while the trouble we're all in right now (do hope you and yours are ok) (– *all fine thank you – Ed.*).

A few observations. Jeremy Clarke's **The Croydon Tangle** was full of interesting stuff. My paternal grandparents lived at Anerley, backing on to the Crystal Palace-Beckenham Junction line. Still in situ when I was small was an east-south spur linking Beckenham with Norwood Junction. It was single track, so trains could only travel southwards. My long-time friend and fellow Southern Electric enthusiast Tony Dyer tells me it was called the Admiralty Spur, probably because it carried Naval personnel from Chatham to Portsmouth during the First World War. Seeing it on your map meant that a hazy childhood memory turned out to be quite correct. From my grandparents' back garden, I remember seeing a steam engine disappearing literally down the bank towards Norwood. The link, never electrified, veered off at the aptly-named Spur Junction.

I enjoyed Ernie Oliver's observations, even forgiving him for being not so keen on electrics. I was fascinated by his account of travelling in the 1950s from his home on the Southern Region's then-called east section on BILs and/or HALs, reversing at London Bridge and heading south to Brighton. I've asked like-minded pals to investigate in old working timetables.

Alongside Ernie's reminiscences, you had a shot of a SUB compartment interior; "Too cramped for you", the caption ending: "Do we miss it – not really!" Oh, but we surely *do* miss those comfortable deep seats.

Finally, the piece entitled The Lines and Stations Dr Beeching Did Not Close. Down the many years since the Doctor's time, I have always chafed at that sort of description of his work. We should remember he was asked to make a thorough report on the real scale of loss-making on the railways. It was for the politicians of the day – meaning the Labour government which took power in 1964 – to make the decisions. They were the people who actually closed so many beloved lines and stations.'

George Hobbs has also been in touch again on the 'mystery image'. 'The picture on p 7 shows the bridge of the LCDR main line crossing the Strood to Maidstone West SER line. The Maidstone line passes, on a rising gradient, under the central span of the steel bridge, the left hand span crosses two storage sidings, where the electric units are standing. The L1 and its train will shortly cross the Medway and arrive at Rochester. (See picture 49 in the Middleton Album, "Dartford to Sittingbourne".) Like you I presumed this was much nearer London!

Secondly, the 2-EPB (not 4-SUB) 5772 on p 38 is about to depart from Higham, at the other end of the Higham and Strood tunnels that were taken over by the SER from canal usage. (See the same book, picture 42.) The Dartford Loop was my local line for many years, though normally I was heading towards London.'

And to show how things can develop, 'little acorns' and all, this is what started the reminiscences piece from **Vernon Jones** we are proud to include in this issue.

'Dear Sir, I am a regular reader of The Southern Way, it brings back many happy memories of my time as a BR fireman in the sixties, based at Eastleigh Motive Power. I was particularly interested in issue 44, 'Life at Eastleigh in the latter days of steam' by John Stubbington.

Although I cannot remember him clearly, we must have many memories in common. I started as a cleaner aged just 15 in March 1961 and believe that when John started I was just about to begin firing. I think it was he who took over my role as 8.28 messenger. He mentions my name in his article, Vernon Jones…

I would like to get in touch with John if he is agreeable and wonder if you would mind forwarding this letter to him. If you should want to publish my letter in a future issue of The Southern Way, I would have no objection. I attach a photo of the framed picture. Thank you, yours sincerely, etc. ,etc.'

Well the result was we did contact John and he was more than happy for Vernon to be put in touch. Pleased to help.

Now a **puzzle** from **Antony Hemans**. 'I wonder if you or any of your readers can help. Would you be willing to publish the following:

My query is that, I have a number of photographs of 'The West Sussex Downsman' Rail Tour, all dated 8 June 1958 and all with Q Class No 30549 and with Set 472 being an eight-car rake formed of LSWR 'Ironclad' Corridors. I know that on that date it was a 'Ramblers' Excursion' and the locomotive travelled chimney first to Midhurst and left Midhurst tender first, as there was certainly nowhere at Midhurst for it to turn, the engine taking its empty stock back to Horsham for servicing. It had begun its journey from Charing Cross, reaching Midhurst via Epsom. People seen in these views at Midhurst certainly seem to be kitted out for 'rambling'.

However, I also have photographs of 'The West Sussex Downsman' with the same locomotive, same route indicator, same rake of coaches (Set 472) and same date, arriving at Midhurst tender first and leaving Midhurst chimney first. It is also seen passing Selham from Midhurst chimney first.

No 5956 *Horsley Hall* trespasses on to the Southern at Purley with the 7.35am Birkenhead to Ramsgate. See accompanying letter from Gerry Nichols.
Sid Nash/Stephenson Locomotive Society

People seen in the view of the locomotive about to leave Midhurst are too smart to be 'ramblers'.

I have been told that the first tour was so successful, that another one was put on a few weeks later. I have been in touch with the LCGB, Ramblers Association and Six Bells Junction. None of them can help.'

We have discussed this ourselves with Antony and various options/possibilities; one train, two trains, we do really need more photographs to prove conclusively one way or the other. Can you help please?

We should also record the sad passing recently of Southern enthusiast and friend of SW, Les Burberry from Aldershot. Les contributed much behind the scenes material and for that and his trust we remain ever grateful. Thanks to Roger Thornton who imparted the sad news.

Finally we should add that in addition to those mentioned, Mick Field, Greg Beecroft, and Chris Prior have all been in touch with similar comments on Strood and Mick Field again re Dover Priory. Gentlemen, thank you.

John Davenport, Stuart Hicks, and others have also kindly sent words of congratulations on reaching the milestone of No 50. I might put the issues together, but it is all of you who make it.

Drifting smoke this time around the can. The less than ideal conditions displayed by No 34089 *602 Squadron*. South Eastern lines of course, but another one for someone to please identify the precise location. (Appreciate not a lot to go on.)

Book Review
Main Line to the South

*The Southern Railway Route Between Basingstoke, Winchester,
Eastleigh & Southampton – Part One*
Basingstoke to St Cross

John Nicholas and George Reeve

Published Irwell Press £34.95

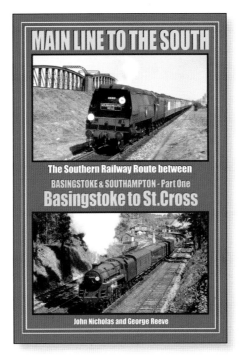

At first glance an awfully long title for a book, especially for one that covers a distance a railway of no more than 20 miles but then the two authors have also found plenty to say.

Coming from the same area as that covered by this book it was a sheer joy to learn new facets of history, recognise names and in other places confirm what I might always have suspected.

The authors have skilfully woven a concise history covering the line, stations and intermediate infrastructure from the 1830s through to the end of steam followed by a shorter glimpse of the decades since. Working details, signal box details, some staff names all add to the mix and whilst it must be said perhaps more could sometimes be said in a few areas, to do so would have resulted in a series that few would probably buy and in consequence be impractical to the publisher; no John Nicholas and George Reeve have got it about right.

What the reader will get for his £34.95 is 296 pages, art paper, good illustrations and plans, the odd one slightly faded or difficult to see the detail, but that could as much be down to the age and condition of the original as your reviewers eyesight! As a random example of one thing I found particularly interesting was the caption to the early view of Basingstoke (p121). This depicts the platform awning with the characteristic pillars supporting this placed at intervals close to the platform edge. The authors refer to this style of awning (and supports) as being of the same type as used by the South Western at Romsey, Farnborough, Farnham and Andover, and go on to say, "The tragic events of 1885 were a clear indication to the company that rebuilding of these awnings would be necessary at several locations." It transpires the death of a guard was attributed to their positioning close to the track.

I can find nothing derogatory to note. The printing is good, the quality exactly what we would expect to find with Irwell Press and it is perhaps best summed up with the oft quoted phrase, 'It does what it says on the tin'.

I look forward very much to the next volume taking the story south from Shawford Junction to Eastleigh and the outskirts of Southampton. After this we are told will come a volume on Southampton; perhaps we could even persuade the authors to continue on to Bournemouth at some point in the future?

Highly recommended.
KR

A Plea for Information...

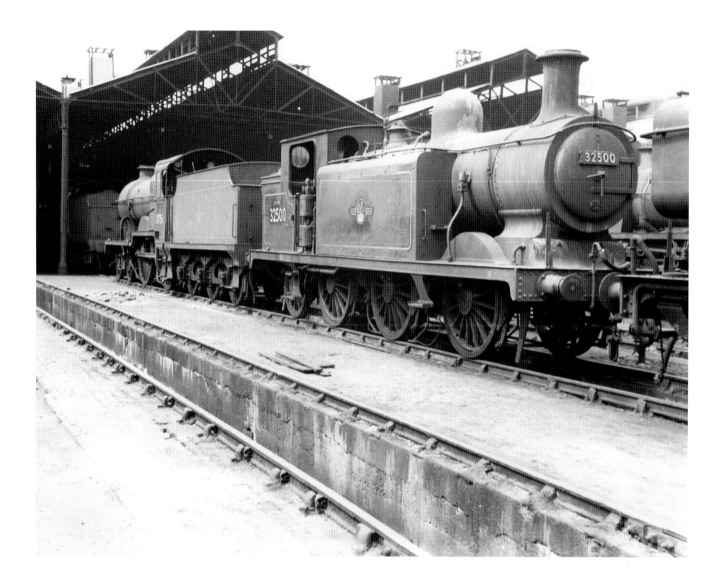

Keith Gunner has alerted us to a recent article in the 'Engine Shed Society' magazine 'Link'. In this the two authors, Ross Woolard and Roger Butcher, discuss the alleged transfer of over 100 steam engines to Nine Elms in 1959 consequent upon Phase 1 of the Kent Coast Electrification. The article has the tempting and shall we say curious title 'Did the R1s really get transferred to Nine Elms?'

Well, it is an interesting and relevant point.

We know of course that some 'L1s' for example did migrate west plus of course the more modern motive power, 'Bulleids' for example, but what did happen to the rest? (Six R1s are being shown as being withdrawn in 1959, but two, Nos 31047 and 31337, survived until the following year.) So was the move of 100 more of a paper exercise that was later cancelled before it actually took place, did someone think 'sent them to Nine Elms', and then realised there was no physical room let alone work for this number? Does this even mean large numbers of engines were thus stored elsewhere?

If you can help please get in touch.

Finally, reference 'A plea for information'. Nine Elms with Brighton and South Eastern engines. Some former Eastern section 4-4-0s we know did reach the Western lines as seen here, but how about the others referred. Can you indeed help?

Southern Way

The regular volume for the Southern devotee

MOST RECENT BACK ISSUES

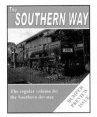

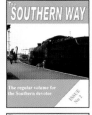

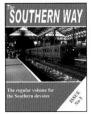

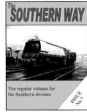
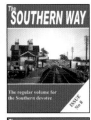

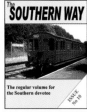

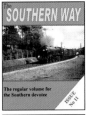

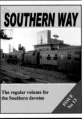
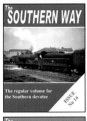

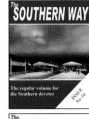
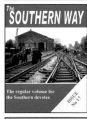

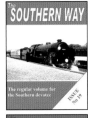

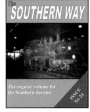

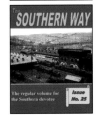

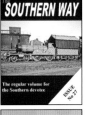

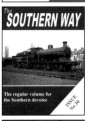
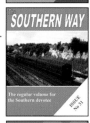

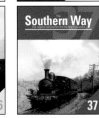
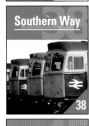

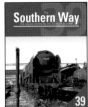
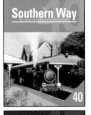

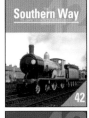

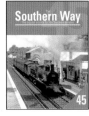

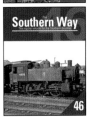

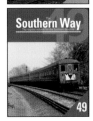
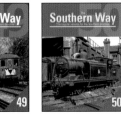
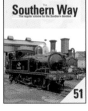

The Southern Way is available from all good book sellers, or in case of difficulty, direct from the publisher. (Post free UK) Each regular issue contains at least 96 pages including colour content.

£11.95 each
£12.95 from Issue 7
£14.50 from Issue 21
£14.95 from Issue 35

Subscription for four-issues available
(Post free in the UK)
www.crecy.co.uk